LUCRETIUS: EPICUREAN AND POET

LUCRETIUS
EPICUREAN AND POET

COMPLEMENTARY VOLUME

BY JOHN MASSON, M.A., LL.D.

LONDON
JOHN MURRAY, ALBEMARLE STREET, W.
1909

PREFACE

IT was impossible either to discuss in the former volume all the Epicurean doctrines referred to by Lucretius, or to give all the evidence for the conclusions I have stated, these being based upon texts some of which are very intricate and difficult. In certain cases a choice had to be made as to points to be left over to the Appendix. Perhaps one or two of these might have been treated more appropriately in the book itself, if space had allowed.[1]

I am deeply conscious of the extreme difficulty of the subject, and have gratefully to acknowledge the value of several criticisms from which I hope the book may one day profit.

The main point as to which critics have differed from

[1] I may mention here the attack (it cannot be called 'criticism') on my book in the *Times* (January 16, 1908). The writer condemns it on the ground of minor omissions, which he magnifies as if they were central points. At the same time, he entirely omits to mention that in the Preface and elsewhere an 'Appendix,' or supplementary volume, is frequently referred to for subjects which there was not space to treat in full. The critic, who is of the extreme academic type, does not attempt to grasp the real 'content' of the book, while in his remarks upon Epicureanism he is satisfied to deal with its merest surface. But, apart from this total difference of standpoint, his criticisms cover only a small portion of the matters dealt with. Notably, he avoids the greater doctrines. While emphasizing details, he does not even name central and capital Epicurean tenets, treated at length in chapters which embody much fresh research. I refer, for example, to atomic Declination and Epicurus's theology, certainly the most difficult and among the most distinctive of his doctrines.

v

me is with regard to the ' Electron.' Several of these have forgotten that the new knowledge resulting from the discovery of radium has in no way destroyed the Atomic Theory as a working hypothesis. No doubt the ' atom ' in the strict sense of the word is now the Electron —that is to say, if only we knew a little more about that particle ! In the essential quality of indivisibility, on which Lucretius bases the fact of law in Nature and the persistence of all things in the world, his atom corresponds to the Electron. The unchangeableness of the atom is a dogma at present demonstrably false. But would Lucretius have accepted the Electron as equivalent to his atom ? I do not think he would. The Lucretian atom has another quality—that of forming groups, and entering into combination with other atoms, to form substances, in which quality it answers to the modern chemical atom, of which the essential property is that it can combine in fixed proportions with other atoms.[1] But what do we know as to the combining properties of the ' Electron '? The doctrine of atoms which has been evolved during the nineteenth century is a conception which chemistry will never be able to dispense with as a working hypothesis, so far as one can judge, for all time to come.

One able critic complains that I have not given ' an authoritative exposition (sic) of the present position of the atomic theory,' including in this the theory of Electrons ![2] In face of the extreme disagreement of the chief authorities with each other and with themselves, as quoted in Appendix V., this critic might well appear to be a humorist. It is as yet premature to think of comparing Lucretius's atom with the Electron, so vague is our knowledge about the latter. If the Daltonian atom persists, and will always persist, as a half-way house to the Electron, it must do this in virtue of some close and vital

[1] This is why Lucretius is fond of calling his atoms 'seeds of things '—*semina rerum*.
[2] *The Nation*, February 1, 1908.

relation (not yet grasped by science) to the final indestructible particles.   The chemical atom behaves in very
important respects as if it were final, and it may be called
' quasi-final.'   Will the processes of atomic disintegration
into electrons ever be brought so under control that we
shall be able to utilize them as we do our ordinary methods
of chemical analysis ?   Some chemists would say that the
former process differs from the latter not in degree merely,
but in kind.

The *Times* critic imposingly informs us that ' Lucretius
was not a chemist. . . .   From his point of view the
atom was the ultimate particle, and, since this particle
is at present the Electron,' I ought to have discussed the
modern ' Electron ' rather than the Daltonian atom, and
to have treated fully the inquiry ' whether (as has been
said) matter is not only explained, but explained away.'
' The total neglect of this question,' he adds, 'is surprising'!
Here is, indeed, logic with a vengeance—logic which
ludicrously defies both the sense of proportion and the
historic sense !   With so wide a subject, before devoting
a chapter to discuss the very conflicting theories of to-day
as to matter being ' explained away ' or not (see Appendix V.), it was necessary to record, and to record in full,
those doctrines of Epicurean science to which the world
owes so great and manifold a debt.   It was not for
nothing that, when modern science was struggling for
birth, Gassendi made the world familiar with the ancient
theory of atoms, with Epicurus's firm grasp of law in
Nature and his reachings after scientific method.   These
were solid achievements, and to set them forth was the
real task which this side of my subject called for.   The
undertaking, though the critic may ignore it, is no slight
one.

The reviewer first quoted considers that the Tyndall-
Martineau controversy as to the ' potency of Matter,'
of which a full account is given, is ' rather out of date
by now,' as is also W. K. Clifford's theory of ' mind-
stuff,' which I quoted as a parallel to the doctrine of

Atomic Declination.   Instead of the latter, he recom-
mends me to discuss ' the far-reaching speculations of
Professor Haeckel.'[1]   On both points I must differ with
him.   As a thinker, Clifford is far more original than
Haeckel.   Lucretius's saying that ' Nature is seen to do
all things herself, and entirely of her own accord without
the gods,' has never been more vividly and suggestively
illustrated than by the famous discussion between Tyndall
and Martineau.   That controversy is by no means out of
date, and will long outlast all Haeckel's philosophizing.
In his gift of luminous exposition Tyndall has something
akin to Lucretius.

Lucretius was not first and foremost a man of science.
One main aim of my book is to treat Epicurean ethics.
I have written from the standpoint of the Humanist,
never forgetting that Epicureanism was not merely a
system, but a rule by which men sought to guide their
lives, and in some sense even a religion.   In this attempt
to estimate Epicureanism from a practical standpoint, it
would be one-sided indeed to ignore Epicurus's attitude
to theistic belief in its bearing on ideals of conduct.

In this volume I have briefly treated the history of the
doctrine of Pleasure both before Epicurus and in our own
days (see Appendix, §§ xii.-xv.) ; but I have been more
anxious in the case of both Epicurus and Lucretius to
show that each of them had heart enough for the making
of ' a moralist.'[2]   Not all who pretend to discuss ethics
deserve that name.   To grasp and allow for the strange
contradictions in the teaching of Epicurus springing from
strange contradictions in his temperament and character
is in itself a heavy task.

[1] See *The Nation* for February 1 and 15, 1908.
[2] And Diogenes of Œnoanda, too, the old man who, in his pity
' for all those who have no knowledge,' causes the main doctrines
of Epicurus to be engraved on the walls of the most public place
in his city !   The inscription of this obscure, ungifted man is
one of the most significant of Epicurean documents, even apart
from the light it throws upon doctrines both of ethics and physics,
as admirably set forth by Usener.

In treating of Lucretius as a poet and philosopher, I
have tried to avoid as far as possible the use of philosophical terms, which are not necessarily a guarantee of
precise thinking, and so often tend to conceal vagueness
of knowledge. I have tried to express myself in the concrete terms of literature rather than in the abstract. The
latter has the advantage of being by far the easier method.
But the danger of abstract treatment is its superficiality.[1]
Its realization of facts by the mere reason is too shallow
to allow of any genuine induction being drawn. It tends
to create an illusory sense of mastery, a false *opinio
copiæ*. The mere concept in the mind is placed above,
and often is actually substituted for, the realization by
heart and imagination of the matters dealt with. As
Schopenhauer would say, in scientific or abstract treatment the subject is merely ' thought '; in literature it is

[1] 'Dialecticorum mens Idearum plerumque inimica.' It is
because such critics do not even aim at inwardness and grasp
that their method ' is at enmity with the Idea.' The entire
subjectivity of this point of view reminds us of the old contention of the Spider against the Bee. Extolling his cobweb, the
Spider says : ' This large castle (to show my improvement in
the mathematics) is all built with my own hands, and *the materials
extracted altogether out of my own person.*' ' In this building of
yours,' replies the Bee, ' you boast of being obliged to no other
creature, *but of drawing and spinning out all from yourself.*' But
the final result is only a cobweb, whereas the Bee (representing
the world's great classics), visiting all the flowers and blossoms
of the field and garden, and with long search and much labour,
' brings home honey and wax . . . furnishing the world with
the two noblest of things, which are sweetness and light ' (' The
Battle of the Books '). What did Sainte-Beuve mean when he
loved to call himself ' the naturalist of souls '? Surely this—
that all true knowledge, in whatever field, must, like the bee,
with his constant excursions into the wide world in sun and
storm, be based upon observation and experience. To the poet
the world, whether of nature or of men and women, has a deep
significance as a living and ever-unfolding manifestation of the
Divine which it cannot bear to the man who lives with mere
abstractions. How wholesome to turn from the latter to any
average page, for example, of Louis Stevenson—and find there
a true bright mirror of real things, every sentence a record of
something experienced, something done, or some vivid aspect

' perceived.' From such abstract knowledge on any subject we learn the truth of it only in an indirect way. It
substitutes, as it were, a geometrical diagram of the
features for the portrait of a face. The result is a figure
of one dimension which, if not too distorted, might serve
as the vague shadow-picture of any Epicurean of the
schools. There is only one Lucretius, and it has taxed
all my powers and demands far higher to grasp the
qualities which make him what he is—the comrade of all
fighters against superstition, the ally of the man of science,
the poet who so loved our earth and every changing feature
of her face, in whom sadness and high fervour are so
strangely blended, who felt for children terror-stricken in
the dark, and who set forth exulting in his bright new-
found weapons, with his heart all on fire to deliver his
fellows from Care and Fear. Nor was it possible to
ignore, as the extreme academic type of criticism would
have us do, the bearing of his doctrines on life and conduct. In this how unlike Epicurus ! ' Philosophy,' he
tells us, ' is a continued striving by thought and discussions to bring about a happy life.' ' Vain is the discourse
of that philosopher by which no human suffering is
healed.'[1] One main aim of the book is to form a severely
practical estimate of Epicureanism, as we find it both in
Epicurus and in the poet, as a rule of life. Epicurus
would have repelled with violence any estimate of his
system which left out its practical aim. Can it save
men from their slavery to appetite, care, ambition ?
By its success in this, he would have said, it must stand
or fall.

---

caught for us of the beautiful earth in the background. Literature is no mere inventory of facts : these must be combined and
interpreted for us by some fine spirit who fills the whole narrative
with a life unmistakably his own, even as we say of a picture,
' Here is a Titian !' ; for we know at once that no other hand could
have painted it. It is the aim of all art to express the meaning
of life. Thus it brings us into touch with the inner reality of
things (see Addenda, p. 196).

[1] See ' The Sayings of Epicurus,' vol. i., p. 342.

The object of the book is not so much to catalogue the Epicurean doctrines or to formulate them, as is done in the text-books of the history of philosophy, as to study their origin in the mind and temperament of Epicurus, and even more to realize them as they react profoundly upon a mind so differently tempered and gifted as the great Roman preacher of the creed. I have also sought to show how each was influenced by his environment, the one living in an age of utter decadence, the other in an age of revolution and revolt from all beliefs. In so attempting, one may come nearer to the ' idea ' of Epicureanism than by any abstract discussion of doctrines, ' explaining words by words,' or by merely tracing their after-history. Lucretius must not be treated as if his poem were a mere pamphlet on Hedonism by an average logician of the schools. In that poem he has fashioned a world of his own; its flaming walls are built out of his own strong spirit; all the beauty and grandeur of the earth (its terror, too) are reflected within it, and men will ever enter in with awe and wonder.

All through the volume I have tried to bring out Lucretius's poetic presentment of his subject, but hope yet to say something further about his distinctive quality as a poet.

Lucretian criticism has suffered from Zeller's long delay in re-editing the volume of his great work which deals with Epicureanism, the latest edition having appeared in 1881. Zeller's broad and sane grasp might well correct the tendency of recent expositors to interpret Epicurus as if he had been not only a thoroughly con- sistent thinker, but a profound metaphysician. These scholars forget that, in the Stoic and Epicurean schools, Greek philosophy turned away from the profound specu- lations of Plato and Aristotle, and resumed again *as its main aim* that which was the professed main aim of Socrates—namely, the search after practical wisdom for the conduct of life. Perhaps Zeller may not quite

PREFACE

realize the value or account for the persistent vitality
of Epicurus's dominant ideas—what Guyau calls his
maîtresses idées—both in ethics and in physics. Doubtless
Epicurus is entitled to walk only in the skirts of the
reverend company of philosophers,[1] but the world will
never forget what it owes him as man of science and
reformer.

Not equally reliable with Zeller in his treatment of
authorities, but of profound interest to the student of
ethics, is Guyau's ' La Morale d'Épicure.' It is a searching and thorough study of Epicurean ethics, the fruit of
much thought, and it is admirably written : every word
tells. Guyau follows up the doctrine of pleasure in its
chief points of development down to the English utilitarian school. His own new ethical standpoint, which,
though rejecting the old sanctions, makes moral obligation a thing inseparable from life and the desire of living,
casts new light on the well-worn problems. Differ from
him as we may, his constant suggestiveness sets the book
apart from all others on the subject, and makes us marvel
how such a work could have come from a youth of some
twenty years.[2]

[1] Thus, his failure is notorious when he has to explain how we
come to possess knowledge beyond what the senses directly give
us. See Giussani's attempt to defend him ('Epicuro,' vol. i.,
p. xxvii, note 2, pp. lvi *ff*., and elsewhere).

[2] See, for instance, the fine criticism on the inadequacy (except
from the Epicurean standpoint of pleasure as the chief end) of
Lucretius's argument against the dread of death. He points
out that there are two very different kinds of the fear of death
which Epicurus has not distinguished—a childish fear enslaved
to the imagination, and an intellectual and manly one, in which
reason plays the chief part. Pascal's saying, ' On meurt seul,'
might be true, he says, if we lived each ' in a complete moral
solitude,' but, instead of this, most men carry about with them
a whole world of impersonal thoughts and generous desires.
Men live each for an aim, whether it be their family or an idea,
and accordingly each man wishes to make of his life a complete
and beautiful work. Thus, our feeling is ' rather a disinterested
repugnance to death than an actual fear of it ' (pp. 123-127,
edition of 1880). I may refer also to the very fresh route of

I have to acknowledge with an increased sense of their value the light which Dr. Brieger's writings have thrown for me not only on passages of the poem, but also on various Epicurean doctrines, and this even when one cannot accept his conclusions. Dr. Brieger, whether successfully or not, grapples manfully with the actual difficulties whether in the text or subject-matter.

Both he and Giussani give great attention to the drift and logical connection of the paragraphs of the poem. Giussani especially discusses these matters at great length, but his numerous transpositions are seldom convincing. Often the text offers problems which are beyond our solution. Scholars have too often wasted labour on the many duplicated and misplaced passages of the poem. They have arranged them in every possible order, but there are parts of the puzzle which will not fit in, and this for obvious reasons.

Giussani's bent is strongly metaphysical. His first volume is devoted to inquiries and speculations round about some main and some obscure doctrines, as to which

---

approaching an old question in the chapters on ' Pleasure as the Chief End.'

In point of absolute sincerity, and the resolve which looks the facts of the universe full in the face without fear, Guyau comes nearest of the moderns to Lucretius. Both have the same intense and lofty absorption in their message ; both are stamped by a violent reaction against the dogmas of the priesthood ; both speak with a strange directness from which all mere literary conventions have dropped away. But in Guyau there is also a tenderness and a chivalrous, perhaps too hopeful, confidence in humanity and its capacity for good which have much of the very essence of that ' Christianity ' which he knows only in a travestied form as something inseparable from miracle-working images and degrading superstitions which blind men's eyes. What could Guyau think of processions during time of drought to conjure a certain Madonna who is ' the best of all for rain,' or during other danger to supplicate some other image which is invaluable against earthquakes ? It is this which explains the closing words of his book : ' In our own days, it is still the spirit of the old Epicurus which, combined with new doctrines, is working upon Christianity and undermining it.'

his results must be received with the utmost caution. Always prolix, his thought tends to lose itself in a cloud of words. Yet his commentary contains valuable help. His constant acute searching of and after the argument frequently throws light on difficult places ; sometimes it leads him astray. He takes little interest in Epicurean ethics, or, indeed, in ethical problems generally. With his highly abstract bent Lucretius's work appeals to him far more on the side of logic than as a poem, nor has he anything fresh to say on Lucretius's quality as a poet.

I am under special obligations to Professor J. S. Reid for very valuable suggestions and corrections here printed, and especially for his searching and masterly examination of the Borgian ' Vita.' The latter task is no ἀκίνδυνος ἀρετή ; the path needs wary treading. It is highly un-critical to assume, as some foreign scholars have done, that because one clause of late and extraneous origin may have crept into the text the document *as a whole* must be a late compilation. That life contains valuable matter which no Humanist could have invented, but it also contains matter (I refer specially to the list of Roman Epicureans) which, while it may contain accretions, yet compels us to weigh the possibilities of later com-pilation, though difficulties enough attach to this view also.

Professor Reid has called attention to some errata and misinterpretations of mine bearing on history. Once or twice I have been unfair to Cicero. It is with the great epoch of the Roman Revolution as with the period of Queen Mary and John Knox in Scotland : historians are divided into two camps, and we find the same event oppositely interpreted according to the side the writer stands upon. Professor Reid's view of Cæsar appears to me an extreme one. On the whole, I must side with Sellar's view, as expressed in his exhaustive and searching criticism of Froude's book, a criticism absolutely unsparing in its candour.[1] To me, Sellar's estimate of Cæsar's character is convincing.

I have also to thank my friend Mr. Hans Gaertner, of Munich, for taking excellent photographs of certain leaves of the Munich MS. of Lucretius, showing the handwriting of Marullus. The copy of the Venice edition of 1495, also containing the emendations of Marullus, to which I called attention as existing in the Bibliothèque Nationale at Paris, contains at first hand at least one known emendation by Marullus not found in the Munich MS. This copy may represent the latest and possibly the fullest version of his text (see note in Addenda).

Thanks are due to the Editor of the *Hibbert Journal* for permission to reprint an article on ' Pierre Gassendi and the Atoms,' now greatly enlarged. I owe special thanks both to Mr. H. A. Webster and to Mr. Thomas Anderson, the former and present Librarians of Edinburgh University, and to their staff, for kindness in extending to me every facility of research during many years.

[1] *Fraser's Magazine*, September, 1879, pp. 313-337. Sellar's verdict on Froude's work is quoted by me in Vol. I. (p. 7, note). The book has also been discussed by Professor Jebb (' Essays and Addresses,' 1907), but his examination of the book, as well as his grasp of the subject, is far slighter than Sellar's.

CONTENTS

PART I

THE BORGIAN 'VITA' OF LUCRETIUS

PAGE

Edition of Pontanus's text, prepared for the press by Hieronymus Borgius, under direction of Pontanus— New details in Preface as to life of Lucretius - - 3
Why does Borgius not name his authority ?—Anonymous lives of Lucan and Horace also from Suetonius—Possible accretions—Professor J. S. Reid on list of Roman Epicureans - - - - - - - 7
Who was Pollius Parthenopæus ?—Notion of an immense gap in the poem could be invented by no sane Humanist 9
Opinion of Ettore Stampini—Reputation of Pontanus and Borgius as scholars and men inconsistent with forgery —Late MSS. at times derived *directly* from an ancient source - - - - - - - - 13
    [Cicero's criticism is discussed, with opinions by Professor J. S. Reid and Mr. Andrew Lang, in Vol. I., pp. 38-43.]

MODERN REVIVALS OF EPICUREANISM

CHAPTER I

LIFE AND WORK OF GASSENDI : HIS REVIVAL OF EPICURUS'S ATOMIC THEORY

The Scholastics utterly ignorant of Science—Their failure to explain any natural phenomenon by the doctrines of Accidental Forms or of ' Occult Qualities '—Molière's satire on the latter—The *Vis dormitiva*—Others fall back on ' Elemental Spirits ' to explain the changes of matter, or on *Archei* as watching over and directing the growth of organisms - - - - - 14
The study of Nature forbidden by law in the name of the Church in the sixteenth century- - - - 17

CONTENTS

PAGE

Pierre Gassendi, in his first book, declares war on the Aristotelians—The University of Paris forbids to teach
against Aristotle on pain of death—Gassendi burns the
rest of his book—His charges against the Scholastics
—His career—He becomes Professor in Paris -   -   20

His preliminary 'Defence of Epicurus'—His great work on
Epicureanism—Its influence on contemporary men of
science—Why did Lord Bacon welcome Epicurus's
atomic theory ? -   -   -   -   -   -   25

Gassendi's atomic theory attacked by the Jesuits as
atheistic—It is said to destroy the belief in Substantial
and Accidental forms, and to be irreconcilable with
Transubstantiation—His defence—The doctrine of
'Twofold Truth'—Gassendi's excessive caution—He
exposes the Astrologers, but not the miracles of the
Church—He anticipates Clifford's theory of 'Mind-
stuff'—His ethics—He adapts Christianity to Epicureanism—His character—His death—'He falls a
victim, not to theology, but to medicine'   -   -   29

What science owes to Gassendi—According to the atomic
theory all changes in matter take place 'mechanically,'
solely by contact and preceding motion of particles—
On no other lines could science make progress -   -   41

He explains Gravity as not innate in the atoms—The atoms
not ultimate, but the first of Secondary Causes-   -   42

CHAPTER II

THE CONFLICT OF THE ATOMS AND THE FORMS

Gassendi entirely dispenses with the Forms—He asserts
that 'generation' or 'corruption' (i.e., the birth or
decay of things) is due solely to addition or loss of
atoms ; that Forms cannot be 'educed' from Matter—
The Aristotelian conception of Matter full of difficulties   44

What was Aquinas's doctrine of Forms ?   -   -   -   47

Spiritual and Material Forms—Spiritual Substantial Forms
subsist by themselves, independent of Matter, with
one exception, the human soul—Embryology according
to the Scholastics   -   -   -   -   -   -   47

'Eduction' of Forms from Matter illustrated from Chemistry
—Objections to Atomic Theory on ground of the doctrine of Forms   -   -   -   -   -   -   48

Relation of the Forms to the Ideas of Plato and Aristotle -   50

Bruno develops the doctrine further—Bruno an extreme
contrast to Gassendi—He denies dualism of Matter

PAGE

and Form—The Universal Intellect is the primary
    faculty of the Soul of the World which we call God
    and as 'the Inward Artificer' instructs Nature in
    accomplishing her works—The method of Nature an
    evolution from within -   -   -   -   -   53
Matter is not a mere potency, as the Aristotelians hold, but
    carries all the Forms within it—Matter and Form are
    one—Bruno attributes to the First Form Goodness and
    Beauty—God not only immanent, but transcendent -   54
The doctrine of Forms next developed by Leibnitz—He
    rejects Atomism—His Monads or 'metaphysical
    atoms'—Leibnitz's 'enchanted world'-   -   -   56
The poet comes nearer to grasping the Forms of things
    than the abstract thinker—A chance-born world—The
    doctrine of Forms fatal to Atomic Materialism -   -   59

CHAPTER III

JEAN-MARIE GUYAU : THE DOCTRINE OF 'SPONTANEITY-IN-THINGS'

Professor Henry Sidgwick's estimate of Guyau's 'La
    Morale d'Épicure'—Guyau's chapter on Atomic De-
    clination, which he calls 'the central and truly original
    doctrine of Epicureanism'   -   -   -   -   62
How Epicurus escaped from Necessity through the doctrine
    of 'Spontaneity-in-Nature'—Spontaneity counter-
    balances Necessity, and produces 'Chance' in events
    and Free-will in man—Guyau's Dilemma—Universal
    Spontaneity in things or else Necessity in the Soul -   65
Effects of such a power in Nature -   -   -   -   72
Guyau's texts examined—Can Spontaneity exist in Nature
    side by side with Law ?—Meaning of term *certus*—
    Meaning of 'Necessity' as applied to Nature by
    Lucretius—Could Spontaneity 'work in harmony with
    Nature'?   -   -   -   -   -   -   74
Lucretius assumed to assert that heavy bodies can 'de-
    cline'—Guyau's main text examined (Lucretius, ii. 243-
    250)—Giussani adopts Guyau's theory—Text from
    Plutarch examined   -   -   -   -   -   78
'Chance,' 'Necessity,' and Free-will in Epicureanism   -   83
What comes of the power of Declination in masses of
    matter ?—Zeller rejects Guyau's theory   -   -   86
Spontaneity as conceived by Aristotle—Its relation to
    Schopenhauer's 'Will'—Effects of such a power in
    Nature -   -   -   -   -   -   -   89

CONTENTS

PART II

APPENDIX

PAGE

I. Origin of Leucippus's Atomic Theory from Speculations of the Eleatic School -   -   -   -   99

II. The Sources of Lucretius's Poem   -   -   102

III. Dr. W. G. Ward on Laws of Nature and Divine
Pre-movement—Sir Oliver Lodge on Mind as a
'guiding' influence   -   -   -   105

IV. Different shapes of the Atoms   -   -   111

V. Relation of Lucretius's Atom to the Daltonian Atom
and to the 'Electron'   -   -   -   -   113

VI. Lucretius's Anthropology:
1. The Progress of Civilization   -   -   -   120
2. The Social Contract   -   -   -   125

VII. Lucretius's Argument for Free-will—Necessity in
Nature and Freedom in Man   -   -   128

VIII. Epicurus's doctrine of the 'Veracity of the Senses'   132

IX. The Invocation to Venus   -   -   -   135

X. The doctrine of Isonomia   -   -   -   137

XI. Cicero on the Epicurean Gods—Theories of Walter
Scott and Giussani examined   -   -   141

§§ XII.-XV. THE DOCTRINE OF PLEASURE.

XII. The Anomaly of Free-will in a Hedonistic System -   151

XIII. The conception of Pleasure as the Chief End in the
Cyrenaics and in Epicurus—Modified by the idea
of Time, it passes into the doctrine of *Utility* -   153

XIV. Insufficiency of the doctrine of Pleasure—Its development in the English Utilitarian school—
Altruism   -   -   -   -   163

XV. Ataraxia (Tranquillity) only the *Condition* of Pleasure   167

XVI. Lucretius's Assertion of Law in Nature—Grote and
Socrates—Did Socrates deny that Laws of Nature
are discoverable by man? -   -   -   168

PART III

Notes on the former volume, by Professor J. S. Reid   -   175

ADDENDA   -   -   -   -   -   -   193

INDEX   -   -   -   -   -   -   198

PART I

THE BORGIAN LIFE OF LUCRETIUS
MODERN REVIVALS OF EPICUREANISM

LUCRETIUS:

EPICUREAN AND POET

NEW DETAILS REGARDING THE LIFE OF LUCRETIUS FROM HIERONYMUS BORGIUS

In the summer of 1894 I came upon a copy of Lucretius (the Venice edition of 1495) in the British Museum which contains Pontanus's text completely transcribed and ready for the printer. The copy was made by the hand of Pontanus's pupil and intimate friend, Girolamo Borgia, a kinsman of Cæsar Borgia, and a Latin poet of note in his day. He was a man of ability, and the intimate friend of some of the leading men of his time. Not only this edition of Lucretius, completed with so much labour, but also a ' History of his own Time,' in twenty books, were left unpublished at his death in 1549. He would seem to have lacked some of the energy and all the ambition of the stirring race from which he sprang.

Borgius was an enthusiastic student of Lucretius, and Pontanus allowed him to transcribe his emendations. As the task was completed in 1502, and Pontanus died in 1503, the volume contains Pontanus's latest revision of the text. Ten pages inserted at the beginning of the volume contain a MS. preface and dedication. Probably it was only the death of Pontanus which hindered the immediate publication of the volume.

Borgius's preface, written in vigorous and graceful Latin, contains some entirely new details as to the life of the poet. This is not so surprising when we remember

that Pontanus was a diligent student of MSS., and
had opportunities of examining many now lost to us.
Even during the lifetime of Pontanus how many an MS.
must have succumbed to damp and ill-usage, or even, as
in the library at Monte Cassino which Boccaccio visited,
been destroyed for the sake of the parchment. The
preface begins thus :

'Hieronimus Borgius lucanus Elisio poo,[1] iuveni
erudito patricio Neopolitano. S. et voluptatem.'

After praising his friend's love of study and the eager-
ness with which, even in youth, he inquired into and
discussed questions of natural science and theology, as
well as the profoundest problems of philosophy—'de
rebus naturalibus et diuinis ac denique de contempla-
tionibus ex intimo philosophiæ sacrario expromptis'—
he goes on to quote a saying of his :

'Sæpenumero enim te dicere solitum memini : Turpe
esse homini non inuestigare ac se decipi sinere, Vulgique
sectari errores.   Præclara equidem et uere homine digna
exercitatio.'

These words remind us how men viewed Lucretius's
poem in that day as a great and daring but godless
work, containing truths which might be disturbing to
theology, but which must be inquired into.

He goes on to say that his own and his friend's favourite
studies attracted both to Lucretius, points out how much
Pontanus accomplished for the text ('quamvis tot seculis
lacer, corruptissimus ac pene nulli intellectus delituerit,
ejus tamen divino ingenio magna ex parte emendatus
in lucem restituitur'), how he gave consent for his
emendations to be transcribed, and describes his own
and Elisius's joint labours in performing this. Borgius
then adds some details which he thought good to collect as
being of importance to readers of the poem, 'colligere aliqua
ad hujus poematis principium non parum necessaria':

'T. Lucretius Carus nascitur Licinio Crasso oratore
et Q. Mutio Scevola, pont. conss., quo anno Q. Hortensius

---

[1] Po is a *frazione* of the province of Massa and Carrara.

orator in foro quom diceret,[1] non parvam eloquentiæ gloriam est auspicatus.[2] Vixit ann. iiii. et XL. et noxio tandem improbæ feminæ poculo in furias actus sibi necem conscivit reste gulam frangens, uel, ut alii opinantur, gladio incubuit :[3] [matre natus diutius sterili].

'Cum T. Pom. Attico, Cicerone, M. Bruto et C. Cassio coniunctissime uixit.[4] Ciceroni uero recentia ostendebat carmina, eius limam sequutus a quo inter legendum aliquando admonitus ut in translationibus servaret uerecundiam,[5] ex quibus duo potissimum loci referuntur, neptunni lacunas[6] et cœli cauernas.

[1] In 95 B.C. Hortensius, at the early age of nineteen, made his first speech in the forum, which gained the applause of the Consuls Crassus and Scævola, who were respectively the chief orator and the chief jurist of the day. The association of Lucretius's birth with the brilliant début of Hortensius is a graceful one. According to Munro, two of the best MSS. of Jerome assign it to this year ; the rest to 94 B.C.

[2] Cf. Suetonius, 'Life of Virgil,' xvii. : 'Poeticam puer adhuc auspicatus in Ballistam . . . distichon fecit.' Suetonius is fond of the word—e.g., 'Nero,' vii. 22-37, etc. It is, of course, difficult to distinguish where the writer from whom Borgius draws gives the exact words of his original authority, and where he is merely condensing from him. I follow exactly Borgius's rather wavering orthography.

[3] Jerome merely says, 'Propria se manu interfecit.' It is in the manner of Suetonius to quote the twofold tradition without deciding for either. Thus Jerome says of the death of Terence merely, in 'Arcadia moritur,' while Suetonius gives the various traditions in full.

Jerome's entire reference to Lucretius is as follows : 'T. Lucretius poeta nascitur, qui postea amatorio poculo in furorem versus, cum aliquot libros per intervalla insaniæ conscripsisset, quos postea Cicero emendavit, propria se manu interfecit anno ætatis quadragesimo quarto [a. 656. Donatus].'

[4] Compare the superlative in Sueton., 'De Grammat.' cap. l. : 'Fuitque familiarissimus Ovidio poetæ.' Cf. Cicero, 'Læl.,' i. : 'Quocum conjunctissime . . . vixerat.'

[5] Compare in particular the passages quoted by me in Vol. I. (p. 41, note 2), and also Sueton., 'De Grammat.,' cap. x. : 'Ut vitet obscuritatem Sallustii et audaciam in translationibus.' See pp. 38-43 of Vol. I., where Cicero's criticism is discussed.

[6] This phrase must have come from one of the lost pages. At ii. 652 Lucretius makes special allowance for the use of *Nep-*

'C. Memmio epicureo dicavit opus. Romani autem
Epicurei hi memorantur præcipui : C. Memmius, C.
Cassius, Fabius Gallus, C. Amafinius, M. Catius, L. Cal-
phurnius Piso frugi qui Polidemum audiuit, C. Velleius
Gallus Senator, Vergilius Maro Scyronis auditor, Pollius
parthenopeus, L. Torquatus, L. Papirius Pætus, Caius
Triarius in primis grauis et doctus adolescens, ut inquit
Ciº. de fi : T. Pomponius Atticus et hic T. Lucretius Carus.'

Two of these names of Roman Epicureans, contemporary with Lucretius, are new to us. Polidemum is,
of course, a mistake for Philodemum (see 'Cicero in
Pisonem,' 68). The other, Pollius Parthenopæus, is
unknown. Many of the names in this list are those of
Epicurean spokesmen in Cicero's dialogues, or else of
correspondents of his. It is curious to find Virgil expressly ranked as an Epicurean. Probus, in his short
life of Virgil, which Nettleship thinks is ' compiled independently from the same materials as Suetonius used,'
says of Virgil, ' Secutus Epicuri sectam.'

Borgius continues : ' Sunt qui putent unum et viginti
libros composuisse[1] et poematis principium hoc esse.
Ætheris et terræ genitabile quærere tempus, et usque
ad eum locum Concelebras quindecim carmina intercidisse,[2] quorum ego opinionem nequaquam probaverim.'

---

tunus for *mare*, and he himself, at vi. 1076, has the phrase *Neptuni
fluctu*. *Salsæ lacunæ*, however, occurs at iii. 1031 and v. 794.
Lucretius uses the word in a very characteristic way, giving it
a vaguer and vaster meaning (see Vol. I., note 4, p. 40). (The
phrase *Neptunias lacunas* also occurs in an anonymous work,
'Auctor ad Herennium,' iv. 15). *Cæli cavernæ* occurs at
iv. 171, vi. 252 ; *ætheriæ cavernæ* at iv. 391.

[1] 'A qua bipartita divisione Lucretius suorum quinque et
viginti librorum initium fecit hoc : Ætheris et,' etc. ('Varro de ling.
lat.,' v. 17). Thus Lucian Müller reads after Lachmann. K. O.
Müller has *unius et viginti*. For the Lucretius of the MSS.
Scaliger substituted Lucilius. Lucilius wrote not twenty-one but
thirty books. Dr. J. S. Reid approves Bæhrens' suggestion that the
first twenty-one books are mentioned together because they were
written in hexameters and the remaining books in other metres.

[2] Pliny, 'Nat. Hist.,' xxxv. 8, 34 : 'Sive (opera) extant sive
intercidere ' (*cf.* Livy, ii. 4).

After dwelling on the corrupt state of the poem, Borgius concludes his preface with a date and reference to Pontanus's share in his work, written after an interval of some lines. The gap contains a memorandum, added at a later date :

'Vale : Idibus Aug. anno dni. M°.D. ii. Neapoli.

'Non ego cuncta meis amplecti uersibus opto,

'Non mihi si linguæ centum sint oraque centum,

'Ænea uox :

'Hos uersus, quos uergilius sibi uendicavit, Servius ait esse Lucretii : unde credibile est multa carmina intercidisse quæ non extant.

'Nonis Julii. M°. D. ii. sub pontano cursim legente et emendante.'

From the closing words it appears that Borgius and his friend wrote down their text immediately from Pontanus's dictation. Why did Pontanus not name the source from which his new data are drawn ? Partly in the same way that the scribes unknown who copied the lives of Horace and Lucan do not state where they found them—simply because these lives were prefixed to the MSS. which they copied, and had no name attached.[1] Yet these lives are now universally admitted to be written by Suetonius. But there is a further reason. Pontanus was at the date of this preface a very old man of seventy-six. But for failing energy so practised a scholar would likely not have omitted to tell us where he found his information.

Along with a number of other scholars, I believe that Borgius's new data are authentic, but mixed with some accretions. I shall not attempt to decide this in the case of each detail. One at least is, as Woltjer has shown,

[1] What were the ancient sources of information regarding the life of Lucretius ? Jerome used a commentary on Lucretius to which he refers ('Apologia adv. Rufinum,' Migne, p. 410). This was probably the well-known edition of Lucretius by Valerius Probus, a grammarian noted for his accuracy, and an older contemporary of Suetonius. Probus prefixed lives, still extant, to his editions of Virgil and Persius, and probably also to his edition of Lucretius. From Varro, Suetonius, and from Probus grammarians would naturally quote.

very probably an inference from facts already known—
namely, the clause 'matre natus diutius sterili,' so curiously
appended at the close of the sentence.[1]   This clause, Dr.
J. S. Reid says, 'may well be a late accretion.   Remarks
of the kind were often tacked on to the end of sentences,
just as forged lines sometimes get stuck on at the end of
paragraphs in poetry (there are several such in Lucretius,
not noted by editors).   The words are in a specially unnatural position for a forger to have put them into.'

These data had, I believe, passed through several
hands before they reached the form in which Borgius,
or more probably Pontanus, came upon them.   Supposing the information to be derived from Suetonius, this
is not inconsistent with the fact that it comes down to us
mixed up with matter from another and later source.
Indeed, Borgius's use of the word *colligere* suggests that
he gathered his data from more sources than one.

The list of contemporary Epicurean philosophers is
composed almost exclusively of spokesmen in Cicero's
dialogues, or of correspondents of his, one or two other
names of note being omitted.   The evident references to
the well-known passage about Piso and Philodemus,
the evident remembrance of another notable passage
referring to Hortensius's marvellous first speech in the
forum,[2] as well as the quotation from the ' De Finibus,'
at once remind us how the works of Suetonius are simply
filled with quotations from Cicero, and references to his
life and writings, several sayings of his being also put on

[1] The medical writer, Serenus Sammonicus, dealing with
sterility, refers this to the fourth book of Lucretius, where this
subject is treated,

' Hoc poterit magni quartus monstrare Lucreti.'

Very acutely Woltjer suggests that some scholar either made the
emendation *partus* for *quartus*, or, by a lapse of memory, exchanged
the words.   The *editio princeps* of Sammonicus is said to contain
the reading *partus*.

[2] He was only nineteen at the time (Brutus, §. 229).   For the
association of the birth of Lucretius with the début of Hortensius
compare Sueton., 'Gram.,' ii., where the embassy to which Crates
belonged is said to have arrived *sub ipsam Ennii mortem.*'—J. S. R.

record. When first I read this list, it seemed to me one
that might well have been drawn up by some early scholar
learned in Cicero. But whence, then, comes the unknown Pollius ? Whence comes the cognomen Gallus,
hitherto unknown, applied to C. Velleius ? and why should
a fifteenth-century scholar single out for praise Triarius ?
If genuine, this list must have come from the general sur-
vey of Roman philosophy, which, judging from the analogy
of the introduction to the ' De Grammaticis ' and ' De
Rhetoribus,' was prefixed to Suetonius's ' De Philosophis.'

The list of philosophers constitutes a problem not easy
to handle. It has been thoroughly sifted by Professor
J. S. Reid, who, if any living scholar, is familiar with
the Roman philosophers of the time. He says :

' The list of Epicureans is in any case not strictly
chronological. The date of Amafinius cannot be precisely determined, but it was certainly earlier than that
of anyone else in the catalogue (unless, perhaps, C. Velleius). Catius died in 45 B.C., and Amafinius is put side by
side with him, because the two are mentioned together by
Cicero and Cassius (" Ap. Cic. Fam.," xv. 19, 2). Pontanus
must have had sufficient knowledge of Cicero to correct
the name Polidemus if he had chosen. Fabius Gallus
is, of course, Cicero's correspondent, M. Fadius Gallus,
known to be an Epicurean from the one phrase, "Epicurum
tuum " in " Fam." vii. 26, 1 (Mendelssohn's MSS. all give
" Fabius " in the three letters which have the name in the
superscription). It is, of course, natural to suppose that
the title Senator apparently attached to Velleius came
from N.D. i. 15, " cum C. Velleio senatore " ; but it is
most improbable that a forger who used that passage
would have inserted Gallus. Has the word been accidentally repeated here from above, or may there have
been a Gallus—an Epicurean who is here described as
Gallus Senator—as an obscure Gallus is described in
" Verr.," iii. 152 ? The prænomen " M." attached to Catius
does not come from Cicero, nor from Quintilian, who
give no prænomen. If, as is likely, the Catius of Pliny

("Ep." iv. 28, 1), is the same, it should be Titus. But some
of the MSS. of Horace's satires seem to give the name
of *his* Catius as Marcus. Pollius Parthenopæus seems
dark as ever. Assuming the words to be correct as they
stand, extant material leads to Pollius Felix, the friend
of Statius, and no other. [This would account for the
epithet, Parthenopæus. Pollius possessed a villa at
Naples which was famous.] If "Pollius" is corrupt, the
man may be either Pompilius Andronicus, who lived
at Cumæ, and was noted as an Epicurean, or Opilius
(Aurelius Opilius) (see Sueton., "Gram.," cc. 6 and 8). But
may not "Parthenopæus" have got displaced, and belong
really to Maro, following the famous epitaph? If this
life, like others, received some late incrustations, this
might be one. A mediæval scribe might well think it
needful to distinguish Vergilius Maro the poet from
Vergilius the grammarian. Removing Parthenopæus,
one might conjecture that "Pollius" is erroneous for Pollio
(Asinius), who may have been an Epicurean. It is
curious that nothing definite is recorded, though Seneca
("Ep." 100, 9) ranks him third among Roman writers on
philosophy (after Cicero and Fabianus Papirius). L. Papirius Pætus is apparently only mentioned by Cicero among
extant writers. Notice that the personages from Cicero's
dialogues are not placed together—*e.g.*, Torquatus and
Triarius are closely associated in the "De Finibus," but
are separated here by Pætus.

'If this list was forged by a Renaissance scholar, the
omission of T. Albucius (perfectus Epicureus, Brut, 131)
is very strange, considering the frequency with which he is
mentioned. Also Pansa would have been in the catalogue
(the Consul of 43 B.C.); possibly others (particularly
Rabirius). It is odd that these should be omitted, and
C. Triarius, not an ardent Epicurean—perhaps not one at
all (*cf.* "Fin.," i. 14)—inserted. It seems to me far more
likely that the list started as an abbreviation of some
ancient source, and underwent some corruption in the
course of time.'

Why does Memmius head the list ? It is only Lucretius's dedication which connects him with Epicureanism at all. Might the prominence of his name suggest a commentary (*e.g.*, Probus's) as the source of this list ?

Who is Pollius Parthenopæus ? The name occurs in an inscription (C.I.L., vi. 3360) said to have been found in Pescaria :

'd.m.cn. pollius parthenopæus atticillæ delicatæ suæ benemer ti. f.'

This is one of the inscriptions recorded by the Benedictine Galletti in the years 1741-42, a number of which are said to have been fabricated by him. I may point out that a name which may be the same occurs in an inscription from Morrone, in the same district as Pescaria (C.I.L., ix. 6078, 132) :

'cn. pollius fec.'

It is, of course, unlikely that Suetonius could have placed Pollius Felix, Statius's friend (A.D. 45-96), among so many Epicureans contemporary with Cicero. The connection of Pollius Felix with Epicureanism does not seem conspicuous enough to induce a grammarian to insert him in this list of names whose associations are so different. It depends on a single reference to his studying Epicurus's book amongst other pursuits of his leisure, yet in the same poem he is spoken of as earnestly studying others of the older poets and philosophers.[1] The designation Pollius Parthenopæus, as Professor Percy Gardner points out, ' no doubt means merely " Neapolitan,"

---

[1] In his description of Pollius's seashore villa, Statius says :

'Hic ubi Pierias exercet Pollius artes,
Seu volvit monitus, quos dat Gargettius auctor,
Seu nostram quatit ille chelyn seu dissona nectit
Carmina sive minax ultorem stringit iambon.'
Silvæ, ii. 2, 112.

Compare the reference to the splendid statues which adorn the villa :

'Ora ducum ac vatum sapientumque ora priorum,
Quos tibi cura sequi, quos toto pectore sentis.'
Ibid., 69.

and belongs naturally to freedmen.' The Pescaria inscription seems to suggest a man of culture and a Greek as its author. Naples, we know, was a centre of Epicureanism. May there have lived there, attached to some wealthy house, an Epicurean philosopher, otherwise unknown to us—a countryman of Philodemus and Siro?

As to the list of Lucretius's friends Professor Reid writes : ' There is really no difficulty about a connection between Lucretius and M. Brutus. No one could well know Atticus without knowing Brutus '; and, we may add, it was hardly possible to know Cicero without knowing Atticus. Lucretius was, like the other three, himself probably a man of rank. Sellar has noted the ease and fearlessness with which he addresses Memmius, who, we may observe, is not included in the list.

Professor Reid agrees with me that the authority anonymously quoted is Varro's ' De Poetis Latinis,' on which Suetonius's ' Life of Lucretius ' was probably based.[1]

The notion of an immense gap in the poem before line 4 of Book I. has neither rhyme nor reason in it. Except here, no trace of it occurs. Does Dr. Woltjer imagine that any ' humanist ' who was sane ' invented ' this ? Pontanus rejects it most emphatically. So shrewd a man would never have recorded it even, unless he had found it in some source ancient enough to justify him in mentioning anything so absurd. Rather does cautious criticism view such a statement (like certain ancient corruptions which occur in the best MSS.[2]) as a sign of antiquity and of independent, even if misinterpreted, tradition. The noted Italian scholar, Ettore Stampini,

[1] See Ritschl's commentary (' Reifferscheid,' p. 516).
[2] For example, the reading πονεῖν ἢ τοῖς θέοις in Soph., ' Œd. Tyr.,' 896. This is a meaningless and most evident interpolation forced into the text, yet it is found in L., and would be a sign of the antiquity of any other MS. in which it occurred. No codex correctus could contain it. Its origin is ably explained by Professor Campbell (' Sophocles,' vol. i., 1879, p. xxvii).

discussing this subject, reminds us how ' the Humanists
have sometimes preserved for us most valuable details
taken from sources which, though authentic, are unknown
to us.'   He condemns the notion of ' including in the same
judgment all the notices found in Borgius's "Life of
Lucretius," as if they were all, indiscriminately, " the
mere inventions of the Humanists," as Dr. Woltjer calls
them.'[1]   This is the more truly critical attitude.

One thing Dr. Woltjer has entirely forgotten.   These
details are handed down to us on the credit of a famous
poet, scholar and student of MSS., and of his secretary,
Jerome Borgia, also a distinguished man of letters.
Ariosto has done him the honour to mention him along
with Marullus in his ' Orlando ' (xxxvii. 8), ' Marullo
ed il Pontan.'   In case he accepted new matter as genuine,
without paying heed to its source, Pontanus had a character to lose as a scholar of note,[2] while, as men, both
he and Borgia had a character to lose if they forged new
data themselves.

Professor Reid remarks : ' I see nothing in the language
of the Vita inconsistent with Suetonius.'

[1] ' Il Suicidio di Lucrezio,' 1896, p. 35.   Stampini instances
the anonymous life of Juvenal, found by Dürr at the end of the
Barberini MS., as sufficient to prove that new data may be
found in such lines mixed up with matter of late origin.   No
scholar could accept this life, with its parade of literary references,
as throughout a genuine antique.   Schanz, while admitting that
this life is one ' elaborated by a Humanist,' recognizes that the
new data in it concerning the life of Juvenal and his family
' spring from a genuine tradition ' (' Geschichte der Römischen
Litteratur,' vol. ii., § 418).   To assume *a priori* that a statement
must be invented because it ' appears for the first time in a
fifteenth-century MS.' is both a simple and an easy, but not
a truly critical, solution.   The fallacy consists in forgetting that
while in most cases a fifteenth - century MS. contains the
errors and interpolations gathered from a succession of intermediate copies, in some instances a late MS. may be copied
directly from a very old one.   ' The discovery of a fragment
of Juvenal in an otherwise unimportant MS.,' says Dr. Reid,
' shows what accidents there may be in the history of MSS.'
(see *Class. Review*, 1899, May and June).

[2] See Munro's estimate of him (Preface, pp. 11-13).

MODERN REVIVALS OF EPICUREANISM

CHAPTER I

LIFE AND WORK OF GASSENDI : HIS REVIVAL OF EPICURUS'S ATOMIC THEORY

In this year of enlightenment and universal education, when science has done so much for the progress and well-being of humanity, with what pity and conscious superiority do most of us look back on the past centuries when even the learned knew so little of the world they lived in ! Think, for instance, of the notions which had to pass for Natural Science in the mind of some professor of theology or philosophy—say, of the University of Paris about the year 1600. He believes, along with the learned Scaliger, that wild geese grow either from a shell or from the fruit of a certain tree, and, with naturalists like Gesner, that pike are produced (as old Izaak Walton tells us) ' by the help of the sun's heat from a weed called pickerel-weed.' He believes, most likely, that the earth is a solid ball set in the centre of the heavens, which form a crystal sphere revolving round it, which sphere again forms the inmost of nine other transparent hollow spheres of crystal, in every one of which is fixed either the sun, moon, or one of the seven planets. True, he knows that a Danish astronomer has dared to assert that the world moves round the sun. But even if the Church had not pronounced against it, he reflects, how can any-one believe that the earth, instead of being the centre

14

of the universe, with sun and other planets revolving
obediently round her, has become merely a smaller
planet in a distant outskirt of space ? How vastly
better informed is the Board-school child nowadays !

But let us suppose our learned man, weary of the
disputations of the schools, sick of syllogisms and the
framers of them, to leave the narrow courts of the University and seek the open face of Nature by the side of
the Seine. Brought face to face with things which are
real, how different is his attitude from that of so many
a ' person of culture ' of the present day ! True, he cannot fix the family or class of the plants which grow by
the water-side, nor can he identify their organs or explain
their purpose, as many an average youth could do to-day.
And yet for him how mighty an impress of the Divine is
on all the landscape ! In flower and tree, in shining
river, in the butterfly flashing past him, in the background of green meadows and blue summer sky, in all
and each he feels the presence of something essential,
something permanent, the Energy fresh from God
to which each thing owes its being and its individuality.
It has never occurred to him to regard all these as a mere
display of blind molecular force, which in its simpler
play produces the frost-crystals, and as it becomes more
complex evolves at last the beating of our hearts
and the consciousness of our brains. Almost as little
could he confuse the frost-flower on the pane with the
living snowdrop. To him all these natural objects are
but the manifestation of an essence or living force which
makes each what it is. May it not possibly be that the
seventeenth-century philosopher, who is so ignorant of
scientific facts now familiar to everyone, realized some
of the bigger problems of this strange world we live in
even more profoundly than we do ?

And yet in the hands of his followers how had that
scholastic philosophy degenerated from its founder's
idea ! Travestied for centuries by the Schoolmen, how
very helpless was it when they applied it to explain any

of the phenomena of Nature! Take, for instance, fire.
Francis of Toledo tells us that ' the substantial form of
fire is an active principle by which fire, with heat as its
instrument, produces fire.' Again, calling to mind that
other things than fire at times produce fire, he goes on
to prove that ' fire can result from all the substantial
forms capable of producing it, in air, in water, or in
anything else.'[1] Again, as we shall see, all changes in
substances—heat, cold, hardness, softness—were assumed to be caused by the entrance or departure of
' Accidental Forms.' The non-professional learned men,
those whose tendency was towards mysticism or magic—
a very large class in those days—felt the need of something deeper, of some more genuine explanation of the
phenomena of matter than these abstractions of the
learned Schoolmen. So they invented for themselves the
doctrine of elemental spirits, little elves who could effect
the changes which take place in matter. Thus Paracelsus, followed by our countryman Robert Fludd,
attributes the phenomena of liquids to the nymphs, of
air to the sylphs, of earth to the pygmies, and of fire
to the salamanders. The action of these little demons
was at least something possible and comprehensible to
the mind : so long as one did not inquire further, it satisfied better as an explanation than to say, as the Schoolmen did, that given substances had the power of attracting, repelling, expanding, or contracting simply because
these substances possessed ' Attractive,' ' Repulsive,'
' Expansive,' or ' Contractive Faculties.' In the burlesque picture of an examination for admission to the
degree of doctor of medicine with which Molière concludes the ' Malade Imaginaire,' the candidate, when
asked to state ' the cause and reason why opium
produces sleep,' answers triumphantly that it is because
it has a ' dormitive faculty ':

' Quia est in eo Virtus dormitiva,
  Cujus est natura Sensus assoupire.'

[1] Quoted by Professor Latta, ' Monadology of Leibnitz,' p. 157.

again, when asked why rhubarb and senna have the power of purging, he answers, because they have a ' purgative faculty ':

'Quia est in eis Virtus purgativa,' etc.

Leibnitz complains bitterly of the hopelessness of such explanations : it is, he says, ' as if watches were to indicate the time of day by a certain *horodeictic faculty* without needing wheels, or as if mills were to crush the grain by a *fractive faculty*, without needing anything resembling mill-stones.'[1] Along this road no progress could ever be made. Disgusted with the hypothesis of ' Occult Qualities,' justly so named, men like Van Helmont and Agrippa of Nettesheim went so far as to assume countless ' Plastic Intelligences,' ' Archei,' spirits which watched over the living creature from the embryo to its full development. No wonder that Leibnitz complains of such men as believing that ' God everywhere makes use of certain vicarious little deities that He may not be compelled always Himself to act miraculously.'[2]

Between the Schoolmen and the believers in magic the door of knowledge seemed closed for ever. But the former were perhaps the more hopeless of the two. Not only would they not enter in themselves, but they were determined to allow none to enter. And in this they were true to the spirit of their mother the Church. For centuries past whoever had dared to study Nature at first-hand for himself had become at once a suspected man, to be watched, spied upon, and promptly suppressed. Few things, indeed, are more saddening than the hostility of the Church towards science in its struggling beginnings. In the sixteenth and early seventeenth centuries the theologians and the philosophers leagued themselves together to stifle it. It was an axiom of the Aristotelian mechanics that bodies fall with velocity proportional to their weight. Galileo attacked the

[1] ' New Essays.'
[2] ' Antibarbarus Physicus ' (Gerhardt, vol. vii.).

arguments supporting this opinion : then when his reasoning was ignored, he appealed to experiment. In the year 1592 he dropped heavy bodies of unequal weight from the leaning tower of Pisa. The physicists and astronomers of the cloister stood by and saw the more and the less weighty masses both strike the ground at the same moment. But were they convinced thereby ? By no means. They persisted in ascribing the result to some unknown cause, and decided that Aristotle was still in the right and the facts of Nature in the wrong. Nay, such bitter hatred did Galileo rouse by this appeal to experiment that he was compelled to leave Pisa. He had committed the crime of demonstrating the falsehood of one dogma of the Scholastic physics ! These dogmas, based on passages of Aristotle or verses of Scripture, probably misinterpreted, were sanctioned by the Church, and no destructive criticism might approach them.

In the same year in which Galileo had to leave Pisa there was born of a peasant family in Provence one who was destined to follow in Galileo's steps and to do much to encourage the direct study of Nature by observation and experiment. Though the world owes so much to Gassendi ; though he, along with Bacon and Descartes, played so great a part in delivering men from the tyranny of Scholasticism ; though his revival of Epicurus's atomic theory had so weighty and fruitful an influence over the great physicists of the generation who followed him, and in particular over our own Newton and Boyle, strange to say, he is very little known in England.

Though Gassendi is far more than a mere disciple of Epicurus, yet his whole mind and thought were influenced by his Greek master in a way which is almost abnormal. His mind was so dominated by the great scientific ideas of Epicurus and Lucretius : he has so completely assimilated Epicurean doctrine : in spite of the gulf of time between them, he is so closely linked to both that the student of Epicureanism cannot afford to pass him by.

To Gassendi each saying of Epicurus, whether in science or in ethics, is a Scripture pregnant with light for his own day. We shall see that the current which drew him towards Epicurus was the necessary consequence of the intellectual problems and needs of the age. But the sympathy between the two was not confined to science : it lay also in likeness of temperament and character ; the chief needs of both men (and specially is this true, in spite of the professed and on the whole genuine orthodoxy, of the French philosopher) were intellectual rather than spiritual.

Pierre Gassend or Gassendi was born of a peasant family near Digne, in Provence, in the year 1592. At school in Digne he composed comedies in prose mixed with verse, which his fellow-scholars used to act in carnival time. He studied at Aix, in 1615 became Doctor of Theology, and shortly after took orders as a priest. Brilliant talents, combined with a genial temperament which won him influential friends, made his career from the very first a smooth one. In 1616 he received invitations to two chairs at Aix—that of divinity and that of philosophy. He accepted the latter, and after this devoted himself chiefly to philosophy, physics, and astronomy, the last two being his favourite studies. For six years he taught the accepted doctrines of Scholasticism with great applause, but he soon found that these offered to thought not an open but a closed door ; sickened with the utter unreality of the system, he rejected it in disgust. During his last year at Aix he gave out theses for disputations both for and against Aristotle. Gassendi's gifts were soon discerned by two of the most important personages in Aix, both well-known men in their day, whose intimate friend he became. One was Nicolas de Peiresc, a counsellor of the Parliament of Aix, the Mæcenas of his time in France ; the other was Joseph Gautier, Prior of La Valette, a distinguished astronomer and mathematician. Wishing to procure him leisure, they persuaded him to take orders, and procured for

him in 1622 a canonry in the cathedral of Digne.[1] He
now gave up his chair. The first book he wrote was
against the Schoolmen or Aristotelians, under the title
' Paradoxical Dissertations against the Aristotelians, in
which the Principal Foundations of the whole Peripatetic Doctrine are shattered.' Of this work two books
were printed at Grenoble, the first in 1624, and the
second shortly afterwards. The book was a keen and
searching examination of the methods of the Scholastics,
enlivened both by humour and by cutting sarcasm. The
boldness of its attack on received beliefs produced a
great sensation.

In the same year Sieur Jean Bitaud announced his
intention to dispute in public at Paris ' against the doctrine of Aristotle concerning Elements and Substantial
Forms.' The Parliament of Paris was appealed to by
the Faculty of Theology, and in September issued a
decree forbidding the disputation, ordering the disputant
and his supporters to leave Paris within twenty-four
hours, and forbidding them to remain or to teach in any
city of the realm. Further, it is proclaimed ' that *on
pain of death* no person should either hold or teach any
doctrine opposed to Aristotle.'[2] This decree was re-
newed from time to time. By order of the King, the
University of Angers in 1675 and the University of Caen
in 1677 forbade any teaching opposed to Aristotle. The
religious communities followed suit. In 1678 the Ora-
torians, in union with the Jesuits, issued a proclamation,
forbidding lecturers on physics in colleges to depart from
the physics or principles of physics of Aristotle. This
proclamation also laid down certain doctrines which

[1] The old town in the Basses Alpes, which so few know, is yet
familiar and vivid to us in the world of the imagination. To how
many in every land is Digne associated for ever by the genius of
Victor Hugo with the good Bishop Myriel ! It was down the
Boulevard Gassendi in the falling night and bleak wind off the
Alps that Jean Valjean wandered, rejected from every shelter,
until the Bishop made him welcome.

[2] Charles Jourdain, ' Histoire de l'Université de Paris,' vol. i.,
p. 195.

must be taught in physics. The following are the first three :

' It is necessary to teach (*L'on doit enseigner*) : (1) That actual extension does not belong to the essence of matter. (2) That in every natural body there is a substantial form really distinct from matter. (3) That there are real and absolute accidents, inherent in their subject, really distinct from every other substance, and which may by supernatural power exist apart from any subject.'[1]

At the urgent advice of his friends Gassendi burned the remaining books of his work.

In the first of the two books published he criticizes Aristotelianism in general ; the second deals with the Scholastic logic, and also attacks the Aristotelian theory of categories. Gassendi here adopts the extreme position that logic is neither necessary nor useful. In the remaining books, of which he gives an abstract in the preface, he discussed the Scholastic physics, metaphysics, and ethics. The modern disciples of Aristotle, Gassendi complains, are so enslaved to their master that they have come utterly to distrust their own reason, and would rather err with him than attain to truth by following other guides. Their dialectic professes to teach the art of reasoning correctly ; in reality it does not aim at attaining truth, but merely at vanquishing an opponent, and sustaining theses on problems which are useless and insoluble. Hence their insufferable subtleties and interminable debates. They are like dogs which never run straight on, but are ever rushing off to the right hand or the left, and running to and fro over the same ground. The Schoolmen pretend that they are nothing less than slaves, and are free to choose whether they shall be Nominalists or Realists, Thomists or Scotists. Yes, says Gassendi, they are indeed as free as a caged bird which can move wherever it likes — *within its cage*. Their main philosophic ideas he calls ' the workhouses '

[1] ' De Varia Aristotelis Fortuna in Academia Parisiensi,' by Jean de Launoy, 1656, p. 76.

(*ergastula*), or, as we should say, ' the treadmills of the Peripatetic prison.' ' Whether they are Scotists or Thomists, Aristotle is their gaoler, who holds them ever under lock and key, and, like birds in a cage, he permits them to flutter along the perches, but never to spread their wings in the free heaven.' Further, they neglect mathematics, and import into physics a host of theological questions. In a word, they have no thorough knowledge of Nature. The ' Nature ' which they study in the schools is something totally different from the actual world without. In its presence they grope and are bewildered, since they have no notion of experiment or observation, and are like persons who have been brought up in the woods, and are suddenly brought into the midst of a great and beautiful city. Gassendi specially attacks the Aristotelian logic on two grounds : firstly, logic is profitless for exact knowledge, because ' to know ' means to know the causes of things, and the causes of things cannot be known by means of the syllogism ; secondly, the syllogism, granting in its conclusion only what is already in the premises, instead of being a true demonstration, is in reality only a repetition. (In his system of philosophy, which appeared just after his death, Gassendi retracts both these charges ; even Induction, he says, has its power of proof only by virtue of being essentially a syllogism.) A certain scepticism is apparent in the book ; there is no such thing as knowledge, he asserts ; we can only affirm what appears to us, not what is ; the doctrines of all the sciences, physics, medicine, metaphysics, ethics, are but conjectural ; knowledge is not meant for man, but only opinion—else why need God have revealed to us the truths of religion ?

The book was a severe and scornful attack, far more upon the Schoolmen than upon Aristotle. Gassendi apologizes for its tone by saying that it is difficult to treat such a subject and not write a satire. Scholasticism, indeed, held the minds of men in abject slavery ;

the learned would not enter in at the gate of truth themselves, and had choked the entrance with their piled-up
volumes of sophistry. The commentary on Aristotle's
logic to which Gassendi refers so pathetically, a commentary in two great folios, which needed two more to complete it, was a type of the studies of the time. So little
did the men of the schools see themselves as they truly
were that they could afford to jest excellently on the
score that they were more in earnest about finding the
truth of the things themselves than about the names
for them. With as much truth did the Pharisees point
to their broad phylacteries and claim to have more goodness than other men. ' Non curamus, inquiunt, de
verbibus sed de *sensis* ' (as if they said, ' Philosophy is
superior to Grammar—as well as to common sense '). . . .
' Jactare non erubescunt Soloecismos esse laudes et
gemmas philosophorum.' No wonder that Gassendi
waxes bitter over these sayings. He saw that the jargon
without which they refused to discuss any subject was
the death of true thinking. We cannot help asking,
What would Aristotle have said, could he have known of
the malice, the injustice, the hatred of truth, the crimes
against common sense to be perpetrated by his followers
in his name ? Doubtless most of them knew him only
through a commentary, based probably upon a translation, and, even with the Greek before them, they had
a veil over their eyes as they read.

One passage of the preface is characteristic. In dedi-
cating the work to his friend Joseph Gautier, he reminds
him of their former intimacy : the book, he hopes, may
prompt him to laughter and call up their old discussions
' both at home and in the country, but especially in the
sunny olive-orchards of Aix, when we were free to laugh
in the same way at the comedy which the whole world
plays, or pretends to play : when amid our discussions
we were free so often to say, " We are alone bv ourselves : we can inquire into the truth without fear of ill-
will." ' To what does Gassendi refer ? Was it the

comedy of fools and wise men side by side on the stage
of the world ? or was it the solemn farce of the lecture-
rooms of the philosophers and theologians who actually
dream that they are seeking the truth ?   Even from his
youth and all his life through Gassendi was profoundly
conscious of the limitations of human knowledge.

Even in this his earliest work, Gassendi, in his preface,
boldly owns his allegiance to Epicurus in ethics ; he
promises to deal with this subject in his concluding book.
If we consider that Aristotle was identified with the ortho-
dox theology, and Epicurus with atheism, we can understand why, even without the special decree of Parliament,
Gassendi's friends advised the holocaust.   The book
aroused great interest, partly hostile and partly friendly.
Gassendi's tact and faculty for affairs helped to secure
for him a still higher appointment at Digne—that of
prévôt or dean of the chapter.   He next went up to
Paris, and devoted much of his energy to astronomy.
In Paris, now and later, he formed an intimate friendship with the sceptical La Mothe le Vayer, and the
learned Jesuit Mersenne, the lifelong friend of Descartes ;
with Hobbes, whose doctrines he strongly sympathized
with ; and with Pascal ; and also was on friendly terms
with Descartes.   Gassendi now visited Holland, where
the most distinguished men of science in his day were to
be found.   During a stay of several years he cultivated
intimate relations with these, discussing and making
observations along with them.   In 1629 the phenomenon
of four false suns, observed at Rome, caused many super-
stitious fears ; Gassendi, in an ' Epistle on Parhelia,' explained the phenomenon scientifically.   In 1631 he was
successful in making observations of the transit of
Mercury, which Kepler had predicted in 1627, this being
the first observation of the passage of a planet across the
sun.[1]   In 1642 he distinguished himself in a philosophical
controversy with Descartes.   In 1645 he was appointed
Professor of Mathematics in the Collège Royal at Paris :

---

[1] One of the large craters in the moon is named after Gassendi.

here, however, he lectured principally on astronomy. Among pupils whom he instructed privately in philosophy about this time was the young Molière.

In 1647 he published his first work on Epicurus—a book which he had written twelve years before, but which he had delayed to publish, doubtless for prudential reasons. In this work, ' On the Life and Character of Epicurus,' he cleared and defended the philosopher's reputation. This was indeed a necessary task. So evil was the repute of Epicureanism, so monstrously false and distorted were men's notions about Epicurus and his doctrines, that it would not have been safe for Gassendi to publish a book professing to revive Epicureanism and make it the basis of a new philosophic system without this forerunner. Gassendi always refers to it as his ' Defence of Epicurus '—*Apologia Epicuri*. The title-page bears the following sentence of Seneca : ' It is my belief, and I say it knowing that those of my own sect (the Stoics) will not agree with me, that the teaching of Epicurus is holy and right—nay, if you can approach close to it, it is austere. . . . It has an ill-repute, and does not deserve it, yet no one can know as to this unless he has been admitted to a close and intimate knowledge of their doctrine.' We find in this book nearly sixteen hundred years later, in a different world, almost the same note of admiration and even of reverence which we hear in Lucretius. Gassendi gives the portrait of Epicurus from a gem which had belonged to Puteanus of Louvain, and quotes the words of the latter : ' Behold ! my friend, still breathing in these features the spirit of that great man. 'Tis Epicurus ; such was his glance and such his face ! *Sic oculos, sic ora ferebat.*' Only the sacred words of Virgil will serve the Louvain scholar to express his reverence.

The preface is characteristic. ' Men may wonder,' says Gassendi, ' that I should defend Epicurus. By doing so I shall not only go against the stream of popular opinion, but shall be thought by the many to have written a work

hurtful to morals and to religion.   Yet how poor a judge
of truth is the multitude !   A question ought to be settled
not by the number of votes, nor yet by the fame of those
who take side on it, but by the weight of the evidence and
of the arguments on either side. . . .   Most men follow
the example of those who go before them rather than
their own reason. . . .   Some sects flourish by the number
of their followers, while Epicurus's doctrines are covered
over and hidden with rubbish from lack of disciples.
None the less ought we to examine whether the grass-
grown path rather than the broad and beaten highroad
may not lead to Truth, a thing so hard for mortals to
find : whether from the neglected and barren mountain
gold may not be extracted which the stones everywhere
at our hand cannot be compared with.   I am not the
one,' he continues, ' to find happiness in shocking the
prejudices of the many, and disturbing a nest of hornets,
but it is a pleasure to clear the character of an innocent
man.   It is a disgrace that Epicurus should be slandered
so !   Even the fathers of the Church have compared him
to the Prodigal Son !   But what if, when we inquire
into the matter more fully, he is proved to have lived a
life of such innocence, purity, and austerity as did no
other philosopher ? if in clearness of vision and ripeness
of judgment he is hardly inferior to any ? . . .   I am dis-
tressed—nay, ashamed—that he should be torn in
pieces by those who, while they pretend to be austere,
live as profligates (qui simulantes Curios vivunt interim
Bacchanalia).   May my arguments at least induce the
more open-minded of Epicurus's opponents to reserve
their opinion.'   To reject Epicurus entirely because some
of his opinions, like some of Aristotle's, are in conflict
with religion would be like pulling up a rose-bed because
roses have thorns.   Such doctrines Gassendi promises
to refute in their proper place, and concludes by affirming
his submission in all matters of religion to the authority
of the Church.

In 1649 appeared his great work on Epicureanism—an

elaborate commentary on the tenth book of Diogenes Laertius.[1] These two great folios contain a new translation of Diogenes into Latin, in which Gassendi's method is to add in italics often a word or clause, at times a whole sentence, of explanation. Then comes an elaborate commentary. As Epicurus's system included logic, science, ethics, and theology, so Gassendi thinks right to intermingle with his commentary dissertations on the most important questions not only in physics, astronomy, even anatomy and medicine, but in the philosophy and theology of his own time. One is struck at first by his astonishing learning. This, however, is well ordered, and does not prevent him from thinking clearly and profoundly. A mere hasty glance into the work seems to justify Gassendi's fear, expressed in his preface, that readers on first opening the book ' might think they had found their way into chaos.' In reality nothing can be further from the truth. In spite of the enormous range of his subject-matter, everything can be found with ease on its proper shelf, thanks to the very complete index and contents.

Probably no other such commentary has ever been written. Things new and old are blended in a surprising manner. Thus, after commenting on Epicurus's explanation of the movement of the stars, he discusses at length ' how Copernicus set the world moving in the last century,' and ' how Kepler, instead of Eccentrics and Epicycles, most ingeniously introduced Elliptics or Oval Courses of the Planets.' After Epicurus's explanation of the qualities of matter, he treats ' Of the Occult Qualities,'

---

[1] ' Petri Gassendi Diniensis ecclesiæ Præpositi et in Academia Parisiensi matheseos Regii Professoris, Animadversiones in Decimum Librum Diogenis Laertii, qui est de Vita, Moribus Placitisque Epicuri.' Below is a portrait of Epicurus from a gem. Editio tertia. Lugduni, 1675. The work is in two large folios of 611 and 458 pages, with double column, besides elaborate contents and index. It went through several editions (1649, 1658, 1659, 1660, 1675), including a greatly abridged one (Lyons, 1658, pp. 1-166).

discussing the belief in Antipathies, Sympathies, the
Evil Eye, Witchcraft, Charms, Antidotes, and so on,
in no credulous spirit, for Gassendi, a true follower of
Epicurus, is prudently distrustful of the marvellous, yet
not blindly sceptical as to the basis of fact which may
underly such beliefs. Epicurus's explanation of Mag-
netism introduces a long chapter on the subject, discussing the views of Gilbert and others (' The Earth an
immense Magnet,' ' The Magnet a little Earth (Terrella),'
and so on, and propounding his own). Again, in refuting Lucretius's argument for the mortality of the
soul, he expounds his own characteristic psychology.

Commenting on Epicurus's theory of sensation, he
discusses ' whether sensation belongs to the soul alone
or to the whole Organism ?' and brings forward a subtle
theory of his own under the title, ' How sensation is produced from particles which have no sensation.'[1] This
last very startling speculation is enough to show that
Gassendi did not lack boldness as a thinker.

Men of science in Gassendi's generation were sick of
Aristotle—more correctly, of the Aristotelians who
imitated Aristotle's faults but not his excellences. The
constant search for final causes in physics had made men
indifferent and careless as to verifying experiment and
patiently interrogating the facts again and again. Bacon
had already expressed in his ' Novum Organum '—that
is to say, the ' New Mode of Inquiry,' the old one being
that of Aristotle—his preference for the atomism of
Democritus and Epicurus over the systems of Plato and
Aristotle, because the former ' assign the causes of particular things to the necessity of matter without any
intermixture of final causes,' and therefore ' their natural
philosophy is more solid and goes deeper into Nature
than the philosophy of Aristotle and Plato.' Gassendi
saw eye to eye with Bacon here. Both of them had
realized that the phenomena of Nature were to be ex-

---

[1] An account of this has already been given at the end of
Chapter X., Volume I.

plained solely by the inquiry into secondary causes—namely, the mechanical laws which govern the motions of the ultimate particles of matter. Gassendi was doubtless first drawn to Epicurean physics because its method was to seek for the causes of natural phenomena strictly within the limits of Nature itself. Himself both a physicist and a scholar thoroughly equipped, he realized the immense value of Epicurus's atomic theory, expounded it in the most clear and lucid manner, and applied it in solving the scientific problems of his time. No mere scholar could have done the work. It was especially through his brief but admirable compendium, ' Syntagma Philosophiæ Epicuri,'[1] that the atomic theory of Epicurus became widely known in Gassendi's day, and influenced men of science all over Europe.

It must be clearly understood that Gassendi by no means intended his revival of atomism as a means of covert attack on Theism. Such a charge was, indeed, brought against him by the Jesuit Peter Cazraeus, a mathematician of some note, and rector of a Jesuit college, who published three letters criticizing Gassendi's treatise on the communication of motion, and especially his remarks in agreement with Galileo on the movement of the earth ; but he also attacked Gassendi's teaching on many other points as dangerous to religion. We can only touch on the controversy. Gassendi's long reply, with its elaborate and somewhat anxious courtesies, shows that he knew the serious nature of the attack upon himself as a dignitary of the Church : the one voice raised against himself would soon arouse the howls of the pack behind. As we follow the controversy between the monk and the dexterous and subtle man of science, the curtain between us and these seventeenth-century controversies which seem so remote drops away. Change the terminology a little, and the problems of that time are, after all, not so very different from those

---

[1] Published in 1649 ; reprinted in 1658, 1659, 1684, 1728.

of our own day—perhaps in their own way more profound.

Among other things, Cazraeus attacked the proposition that the atoms have no secondary qualities, such as heat, cold, colour, etc., as a doctrine hostile to religion on one very vital point. ' If all the changes producing heat, cold, colour, scent, taste, and other qualities are nothing but motions of infinitely small atoms in space, then the Accidental Forms (*Formæ Accidentales*) are done away, and it is far more difficult for them to be conceived of or to exist apart from all Substance. What, then, is to become of the sacred mysteries of our religion ?' (It was the doctrine of Scholasticism, recognized by the Church, that the qualities of matter, heat, whiteness, fragrance, and so on, are metaphysical entities having a real existence, entitled ' Accidental Forms '; and it was held that these entities might even exist—as, for example, ' whiteness '—' by supernatural power apart from the subject.') In the hands of the theologians the doctrine of Accidental Forms played an important part, as explaining the miraculous change undergone by bread and wine in the Mass. It was held that the substance of the bread and wine was removed in the Eucharist, and the ' Accidentals ' alone of each remained. We need not wonder if no teaching was tolerated which could in any way undermine the implicit faith in that mighty miracle which the simplest parish priest had the power to work every Sunday, at the solemn moment when the bell tinkled and he raised the Host, and God came down in visible form before human eyes ! One thinks of the dream of Peiresc shortly before his death, which Gassendi relates in his friend's life : how Peiresc fancied himself to be attending Mass, when suddenly the roof of the chapel fell in, and at the first alarm the officiating priest was in the act of flying panic-stricken, when Peiresc called to him, ' *You afraid when you hold God in your hands !*'

Gassendi dexterously evades this objection. The doctrine of atoms is merely a way of explaining the action of heat, cold, scent, etc., the nature of the heat of fire, the sweetness of honey, and so on. These qualities of things are not done away with by accepting the atomic theory. (Gassendi knows well that this is not the point in question. The Schoolman had good reason to fear that mere logical abstractions, such as the Accidental Forms and the Atoms, could not thrive together.) 'The most august mystery of Transubstantiation can be defended as well, if we suppose the qualities of the bread and wine to be due to the arrangement of their atoms, as if we suppose these qualities to be essential attributes of Matter.'

The Jesuit Father's next charge is a serious one. 'A yet further danger threatens. If Birth and Death are nothing but the local motions of the atoms, 'tis all over with the doctrine of Substantial Forms !' (' Conclamatum est de Formis Substantialibus !'). The Scholastics used the word ' Form ' to denote the Cause of a thing, not an exterior, but a permanent and essential Cause.[1] And, be it remembered, they identified the Immortal Soul with the ' Substantial Form of a man.' It is little wonder if men felt that the question was of something more than logic, and that great realities hung upon it.

As to the doctrine that Birth, Death, etc., are due to the motion of the atoms, Gassendi defends himself indignantly. 'This,' he says, 'is a mere doctrine of physics, and must not be transferred to Theology. The asserters of atoms are no more at fault than Aristotle, with his doctrine of " First Matter," which he conceives eternal and uncreated. If the Scholastics retain this doctrine, with the exception that it is produced by God, what forbids us to retain the atoms with the same modification ?' As to the soul of man, we may again follow the Aristotelians. ' Just as the Rational Soul is by them made an exception to the general proposition

[1] Aquinas says that ' God is by His essential nature Form,' and our own Spenser :

' For Soul is Form, and doth the body make.'

regarding Forms educible from Matter [the Substantial
Forms], in the same way it may be made an exception
to the proposition regarding the Accidental Forms. Thus
the Soul itself may in future be regarded as properly a
Substance, inasmuch as it exists by itself, unlike the
other " Forms," as to which common sense is unable to
tell whence or how they derive their substantial Entity
as something distinct from Matter.'

But what difficulties, he continues, attend the belief
in Forms !

Gassendi concludes by saying : ' Finally, whatever
Holy Church prescribes, that I am prepared to believe,
and to hold not only Epicurus and Democritus, but even
Aristotle and Plato and all other philosophers, of no
account whenever they propound anything hostile to
religion ; and I am prepared to count even the light of
reason as nothing in comparison with the light of faith,
and, in particular, as to the possibility of the existence
of Substance without Accidents or Accidents without
Substance [as the Aristotelians asserted], to admit that
God can do even what is unthinkable by us, and that the
measure of His action is nothing less than His infinite
power.'[1]

Evidently Gassendi's piety was quite beyond suspicion.
Could such a man as Gassendi ever have believed in
the existence of real accidents ?   Two opinions may be
held regarding the good faith of such a passage as that
just quoted.   It does not follow that the more apparent
opinion is the true one.   In Gassendi's time, and for
some centuries before him, many men believed, and some
dared to say, that there was such a thing as ' Twofold
Truth '—namely, that two doctrines which were mutually
contradictory might both be true, one in philosophy and
the other in theology.[2]   The doctrine was expressly con-

[1] See chaps. xxi.-xxv. of Gassendi's answer to Cazraeus, entitled,
' De Proportione qua gravia decidentia accelerentur,' published
in 1646.
[2] ' Averroes et l'Averroisme,' by Ernest Renan, 1861, pp. 259
and 275.

demned by the Synod which met in Paris in 1277. ' They
pretend that there are things true according to philosophy,
yet not true according to faith, as if there were two
opposite truths.' The Pope, by a special Bull, gave orders
to the Bishop of Paris to seek out and punish those holding
such a belief. The doctrine was Averroistic, and was
vehemently attacked by Raymond Lully, who maintained
that, if Christian dogmas were absurd in the eyes of
reason, and impossible to be understood, it was not
possible that they should be true from any other point
of view.

Gassendi's sincerity has been gravely questioned—on
the whole, it is probable, very unjustly. Thus Lange
sees in Gassendi's attempt to combine Epicurean physics
with the belief in God and Providence nothing but an
astute precaution to save himself from the Inquisition.
We cannot doubt that Epicurus's practical atheism
was genuinely repellent to his mind. He defends at
length his belief in Immortality and in Providence in
various chapters, each headed ' Contra Epicurum.'
When, after twenty-two of the hundred sections of his
' Syntagma Philosophiæ Epicuri,' Gassendi adds a
' Refutatur ' with a reference to the section of his longer
work on Epicurus where the doctrine in question is combated, doubtless he has an eye on the Inquisition, and on
charges which the reviver and defender of Epicurus's
system might well expect. The burning of Bruno at
Rome in 1600, and of Vanini at Toulouse in 1619, were
still fresh in men's minds. In 1642, only seven years
before Gassendi's great book on Epicureanism was published, had not Galileo died in prison, a victim to the
bitter enmity of the Jesuits ? Did Gassendi resolve that,
even at a certain cost of sincerity, he should not be made
a victim until he had done his work ? Not all men of
science are gifted with the intrepidity of Copernicus—
' the man whose soul was free,' as Kepler calls him.
And yet Gassendi could heartily admire the uncom-
promising character of the older astronomer. ' Copernicus,'

he says, ' could not be diverted one whit from justice and impartiality, either by fear or violence, by entreaties or by bribes.' Well was it for Copernicus that the first copy of his book ' On the Orbits of the Heavenly Bodies ' reached him only on the day of his death in 1543 ! The Order of the Jesuits was founded in 1540.

It can hardly be maintained that Gassendi was sincere in his references to Copernicus. The Church had made it plain that no one must dare, on severest penalty, to defend him. Gassendi had much to lose ; he was a man in high place, a professor in the University of Paris and a dignitary of the Church. In his reply to Cazraeus he affirms that the doctrine of Copernicus has never yet been expressly condemned by the Church, and that the sentence against Galileo was passed only by a Congregation of Cardinals, and has not the authority of a general pontifical decree. Should a decree of the latter kind be passed, he is prepared, he says, ' at once to embrace it absolutely, and to receive it, as the saying goes, with the most blind obedience.' One hopes that these words are ironical ; to us they can appear nothing but effrontery.

Every disciple of Epicurus was the natural enemy of all impostors and pretenders to occult knowledge. Gassendi was no exception. Thus he ably demolished the system of the famous Dr. Fludd, the English Alchemist, Rosicrucian, and Theosophist,[1] and also exposed the

[1] Robert Fludd, a London physician, was a pretender to occult knowledge, whose system then attracted much notice. God, he holds, is one with the world, yet distinct from it. He is specially present in the sunlight ; He is apparently identical with the ether, which is the Soul of the world and the principle of all life. God does not work by second causes—this Fludd calls an ' Ethnic ' (or heathen) doctrine ; He is immediately present and active in all the workings of Nature. As the Book of Job says : ' When God bloweth from the north, frost is given,' and ' He thunders with a loud voice.' The Bible, interpreted theosophically, is the source of all true science, which of itself can only confirm revelation. To rely, therefore, upon Science which is independent of the Bible, such as that of the Greeks, is a horrible impiety. With Paracelsus he holds that man is a microcosm, and that a profound inner relation exists between him and the macrocosm, the universe.

impostors who called themselves 'Judicial Astrologers,' and pretended to base their results on science. Many men of learning were devout believers in astrology. One of these, his colleague Morin, the Professor of Mathematics, took advantage of Gassendi's being in weak health publicly to predict his death in July, 1650, but he proved a false prophet. Early in life Gassendi had plunged into the study of astrology, but he soon discovered its illusions, and his book did much to bring it into disrepute.[1] But for him the delusion might have lasted much longer. Yet we do not find him exposing with equal frankness the miracles of the Roman Church—for example, the cures wrought by the bones of the Saints. Such a man cannot have accepted these. Gassendi was eminently cool-headed and open-minded. An instance of this is seen in the calm analysis which he applies to a dream of his friend Peiresc, which was fulfilled in every detail the next day. While on a journey, Peiresc dreamed that he was at Nismes, and there was offered by a goldsmith a rare gold coin of Julius Cæsar for a certain sum, far below its value. Next day he continued his journey to Nismes, and was there offered by a goldsmith the identical coin, and for the exact price which he had dreamed. Gassendi remarks that while there would have been nothing wonderful in any one of the items being thus anticipated, it was surprising that all the details of his dream should be fulfilled, but refuses to see anything supernatural in the occurrence. His enemy, Morin the astrologer, being asked why Gassendi should conceal his opinions, said : ' Do you know why he dissembles ? It is for fear of the atoms—the little fire-atoms, I mean.' No doubt he stood more in danger of losing his valuable offices than of an *auto-da-fé*. But Gassendi was a man of warm heart, and probably he shrank from the painful wrench of breaking with his many friends who were Churchmen.

Worn out by excessive labours, Gassendi's lungs were

[1] Translated, 'The Vanity of Judiciary Astrology.' London, 1659.

attacked, and in 1648 he had to leave Paris for a residence
in his native air. Shortly after his return, in 1653,
another severe illness attacked him, from which he never
recovered. As he lay dying, conscious of his flagging
pulse, and calling up the many scenes of a long life of
splendid industry in many a varied field, rising from
honour to honour, until the peasant's son had become
the associate of the foremost men of the time, as if
summing it all up, his last words were : ' And this is the
life of man !' (*Voilà ce que c'est que la vie de l'homme*).

Gassendi died in his sixty-third year. ' He did not
fall a victim to theology, because he was destined to fall
a victim to medicine,' says Lange. Having fallen ill of
a fever, he was bled fourteen times, and before his death
he said that his over-submissiveness to his physicians had
cut short his life. He had been fond, too, when with his
friends, of jesting about the physicians of his day and
their methods. Was Boileau thinking of the manner of
Gassendi's death when, in 1674, there being a movement
to procure from the French Parliament an official con-
demnation of the philosophy of Descartes, he composed
his famous ' Burlesque Decree in Support of the Doctrine
of Aristotle, pronounced in the High Court of Parnassus
in Favour of the Masters of Arts, Physicians, and Pro-
fessors of the University of Stagyra in the Land of
Chimeras.' The Faculty of Medicine complain that ' one
unknown, named Reason, . . . has intermeddled in
curing, and has, actually and in fact, cured ' many cases
of fever, both intermittent and continuous, ' by means
of quinine and other drugs, unknown to the said Aristotle
and his predecessor Hippocrates, and this without bleed-
ing, purging, and evacuation—a course which is not only
irregular, but wrongful and contrary to right use, the
said Reason never having been admitted a member of the
said Faculty.' The Court in reply ' forbids Reason and
his adherents for time coming to cure fever by drugs not
approved by the ancients, and, in cases of irregular cures
by these drugs, permits doctors of the said Faculty to

restore the patients by the use of their ordinary medicines
to the state of fever in which they were before, so that
they may be treated according to the rules, and, if they
do not recover, may at least be conducted to the other
world sufficiently purged and evacuated.' The jesting
is bitter indeed, but what wonder ?

Gassendi's own system of philosophy, which is far more
dogmatic than his other works, was not published till
three years after his death.[1]

It was not merely Epicurus's physics which Gassendi
approved. He found himself also in agreement with his
logic and his psychology. Even Epicurus's ethics seemed
to him more in harmony with human nature than those
of Plato or Aristotle. Thus Gassendi conceived the idea
of making Epicureanism the basis of a new philosophical
system. In doing this he found it necessary, on the one
hand, to correct the errors of Epicurus in physics by recent
discoveries, and, on the other, to remove from it those
doctrines which jarred with Christian theology. Over
five-sixths of the work are devoted to physics, in which
subject he includes metaphysics, and even theology,
since physics includes speculations regarding the whole of
nature. Since his first book was written his opinions on
the importance of Logic have greatly altered ; he bases
his own Logic largely on that of Aristotle, which he
commends. His psychology is founded on that of
Epicurus, the soul being supposed to consist of an immaterial spirit or rational soul (answering in its functions
to the highly subtle *animus* of Epicurus) and of a material
part, the sensitive soul (answering to Epicurus's *anima*),
which is spread through the body. (Thus he escapes from
Lucretius's strongest arguments against immortality—
the diseases or passions of the mind affect only the
sensitive, but in no wise the rational, soul.) Gassendi's
psychology is in many respects original, and has largely
influenced later thinkers, especially Locke and Condillac.
Neither of these ever owns him as his master, yet, says

[1] 'Syntagma Philosophicum,' 1658.

Damiron, ' there are few remarkable ideas in the systems
of both which are not found, either implied or developed,
in Gassendi.'[1]

Gassendi's daring theory of a gradual and imperceptible
development of consciousness, mounting up from atoms
to living things, has been already described in the chapter
on Atomic Declination, a doctrine which possibly suggested it. ' It cannot absolutely be said that conscious things come from non-conscious, but rather from
particles which, though they do not actually possess
consciousness, nevertheless actually are or do contain
the elements of consciousness (*principia sensus*).' By
this suggestion, so cautiously made, of ' elements of consciousness' in the atoms, Gassendi anticipated two
hundred years ago Clifford's remarkable theory of ' Mind-
Stuff.' Gassendi's theory had a deep influence over
later thinkers in France. Diderot, writing in 1754 and
1769, assumed sensation to be immanent in all matter,
and to pass into consciousness in the animals.[2] In an
earlier writing he says that ' the degree of consciousness
possessed by the molecules must be a thousand times
less than that which the All-Powerful has granted
to those animals which are lowest in the scale of
life.'[3] Again, Robinet, in 1761, attributed to all the
particles of inorganic matter sensation without self-con-
sciousness, which doctrine he combined with a belief in
evolution.[4]

Gassendi is disposed to see something approaching to
consciousness even in inanimate matter; notably this
appears in his explanation of the magnet. The iron is
impelled to the magnet ' by a kind of desire.' Diffused

[1] Damiron, ' Histoire de la philosophie en France au XVIIme
siècle,' vol. i., p. 451.
[2] See especially his remarkable dialogue, ' D'Alembert's
Dream.'
[3] ' Interprétation de la Nature,' p. 203.
[4] In his works, ' On Nature,' 1761, and ' Philosophical Reflec-
tions on the Natural Gradation of the Different Forms of Life,
or the Attempts of Nature in learning to make Man,' 1767.

through the iron there are particles of some finer substance, ' something akin to soul.' The magnet attracts to itself this, ' the very soul, as it were, of the iron,' which carries with it the mass. Gassendi shares with Lord Bacon the notion that something like soul runs through the whole of Nature. This helps us to understand the remarkable simile which Gassendi uses to explain the action of gravity. The stone falls because ' it feels the earth ' (*sentit terram*). Its fall can only be explained because something comes to it from the earth and draws it downwards. ' It is very like the case of a boy who is attracted towards an apple; it is necessary that the apple should transmit either a picture of itself to his eye or its odour to his nostrils before the boy is drawn to move towards it.'[1]

In the field of morals Gassendi's aim was to reconcile Epicurus's utilitarian ethics with Christianity. A strange attempt ! But Gassendi does not realize this ; his intuitions do not go deep in these matters. (Yet might not any refined doctrine of Pleasure seem more wholesome than the asceticism preached in his day by a corrupt Church ?) The first principle which he lays down among what he calls ' the chief natural laws ' of morality is, ' Each one seeks only his own well-being and interest, and regulates his opinions and actions accordingly.' Such a theory ignores the leanings towards good in human nature—the gleams of virtue which are found even in the grossest and basest. ' Nor,' says Damiron, ' was Gassendi ignorant of this ; he could not be ignorant, he who was so excellent in all his life. But he had his system, and his system caused him illusion—a sad illusion, since it checked him at the most apparent and lowest sides of our nature.' Taking Epicureanism for his capital doctrine, he seeks to reduce Christianity to it, to explain the latter by the

---

[1] ' Id persimile est ac dum puer versus pomum fertur ; . . . et necesse est ut pomum transmittat aut sui speciem in oculum aut sui odorem in olfactum, ut in ipsum puer rapiatur ' (' Anim·adversiones,' vol. i., p. 245).

former—in short, to adapt Christianity to Epicureanism.
' He attempts to reconcile the two, at one time by resolving
one opinion into another, at another by maintaining both
opinions together, but he does not succeed.'[1]

Gassendi was largely gifted with humour, and was fond
of indulging it, but only in the society of his intimate
friends.   When consulted on any question, he used to
give his opinion with great caution ; it was his habit
to insist on the limits of our knowledge.   He is fond
of the phrase *Videtur*, ' It would appear.'   He knew
by heart many thousand lines of the Greek, Latin,
and French poets, including, it is said, the whole of
Lucretius.

Various traits of Gassendi's character recall Epicurus.
He was a man of great natural kindness and generosity,
and was greatly loved, not only by his many friends, but
by all who knew him.   When he visited Digne, the
people would leave their shops and their work in order
to welcome him : he had friends in all ranks : all were
proud of his renown : throughout Provence he was called
' the holy priest.'   He was a man of astonishing industry :
he rose regularly at three or four, and spent over twelve
hours a day in study.   We are further reminded of
Epicurus by his extraordinary temperance, bordering on
asceticism.   ' His life,' we are told, ' was more austere
than that of the anchorets '; he never drank wine, and
seldom ate meat.   He was a man of singularly calm and
even temper : ' Nothing could disturb him, never did he
fall into a passion ; he seemed prepared for everything,
whether good or bad.'[2]   As in Epicurus, so in Gassendi
there seems to have been no touch of self-indulgence ;
his pleasures were entirely those of the intellect and of
friendship.   Doubtless he hardly knew what the temptations of ordinary men were, still less those of the many

[1] ' Histoire de la philosophie en France au XVIIme siècle,'
vol. i., p. 487.
[2] ' Vie de Pierre Gassendi,' by Joseph Bougerel (Paris, 1737,
pp. 431 and 455).

whose temperament pursues them ever like a beast of
prey, and realized no more than Epicurus did the dangers
of the doctrine of Pleasure. May we say that the inconsistency in his system, due to his attempt to adapt
together Epicureanism and Christianity, is reflected in
the contradictions of his own life ?—the daring thinker,
the tireless, self-denying worker side by side with the
opportunist who retracts his profound convictions from
considerations of place and safety. Compared with him,
Epicurus was consistent. Gassendi's temperament, in
which the intellectual easily dominated, excluding violent
passions and most temptations, his career of unbroken
success, and his entire absorption in research, may have
hindered him from grasping with any profound conviction the more inner and organic truths of religion, and
from realizing how essential is the antagonism between
them and utilitarian ethics.

Looking at Gassendi's work as a whole, we must call
him bold, or he never had dared to write what he has
written ; yet cautious and wary to a degree, or he would
have ended his days in some dungeon of the Inquisition
ere half his work was done. He never repeated the boldness of his first attack upon the Aristotelians. He was
not only an acute philosopher and a profound scholar,
but he kept abreast of his age in the whole field of science.
Thus in his student days in Aix he attended the demon-
strations in anatomy, and later he used to make dissections,
both alone and in company with his friend, Nicolas de
Peiresc. Though he made no discovery of importance,
yet European science owes him much. In an age when
the Aristotelians had become the gaolers of the mind,
he realized the value not of merely Epicurus's atomic
theory, but also of his scientific method—namely, the
study of phenomena in themselves. Thus he substituted
observation of facts for the eternal hypotheses and
theories of the Schoolmen. And by his own practice in
various branches of science, he enforced and drove home
this lesson to his own age. None was more needed.

With all his zeal for physical science, Gassendi sees its limitations with surprising clearness. Repeatedly he asserts that the mere analysis of things into their first elements is not sufficient to explain them. Think of the unseen agents ever busy in a living body, animating it, nourishing it, repairing its losses. There is a power here at work past our grasping : no microscope will ever reveal it ; neither our intellect nor our senses are adequate to the task. *Non sumus natura ad hoc comparati.*[1]

Epicurus's theory of atoms, assimilated and revived by Gassendi, did more than merely put to flight the ' Occult Qualities ' and the Elves. It was of invaluable service to European science, struggling for its birth. According to it, all changes in matter take place ' mechanically,' solely ' by contact and preceding motion,' or, according to Leibnitz, ' in a manner which is intelligible.' On no other lines could the sciences make progress.

What, then, is the exact place of the atoms in Gassendi's system ? The atoms, he holds, are self-moving, and are the cause of the movements of all bodies. God, in creating them, has implanted in them the internal energy of motion which we call gravity, and He is ever renewing it. They are never at rest, always moving at the same speed, even when combined in matter. Their motion is the source of all the energy in the world.[2]

Gassendi insists that gravity appears to be not so much a quality existing in the atoms and in all bodies as a force imparted to them from the magnetic attraction of the earth.[3]

Epicurus held that the unceasing movement of the atoms is innate in them from all eternity. Gassendi rejects this notion. Repeatedly and emphatically he asserts that this inherent capacity of motion has been

---

[1] See especially vol. ii. of edition of 1658, pp. 557-560 ; also passages quoted by me in Volume I., p. 240.

[2] ' Animadversiones,' vol. i., pp. 118 *ff.*, 165.

[3] *Ibid.*, p. 167.

bestowed on them at the beginning of the world by God. The atoms, he says, must not be considered as the Primary Cause, although they may be held the first or most remote among Secondary Causes.[1] It is not surprising that his enemies (as does also Lange) viewed him as having thus set the machine of the world going by a Divine hand merely as a compliment to theology, intended to disguise the fact that, as they assert, he leaves God entirely out of his system. Yet, in point of fact, He plays a very real part there.

Gassendi's view has been thus summed up : ' At creation God gave to matter certain determinations which it preserves.' The nature of the universe depends on these ' guiding determinations ' given to the atoms, which prescribe the development that they are to follow. Therefore, we cannot ' begin with the atom,' but ' are compelled to deduce from the nature of the universe that there is something besides the material cause, some Power which can supply the elements of law and order.'[2] Thus, Lucretius's primary doctrine of the reign of law is now turned against the materialist.

[1] In one noble passage Gassendi begins by saying that ' the world has not been created by God in order to be immediately abandoned by its Author,' and shows in conclusion how God works by means of Secondary Causes, ' though without doing violence to these or inverting the order of Nature,' and that it is the business of the physicist to inquire into these Secondary Causes. (See the section, ' Esse Deum Rectorem Mundi Animadv.,' vol. i., pp. 378-381.)

[2] I quote from a book which has just appeared on ' The Philosophy of Gassendi,' by Professor G. S. Brett (p. 224 ff.). Some criticisms on it will be found at the end of Chapter III. I have not been able to verify the passage quoted above so as to say how far it expresses Gassendi's own opinion, how far an inference drawn from it.

CHAPTER II

THE CONFLICT OF THE ATOMS AND THE FORMS

THE Scholastics regarded Matter as vile and mean in comparison with Form. To them Matter was a thing absolutely passive, which acquired a real existence only through Form. Thus a modern Scholastic like Father Harper writes : ' Primordial Matter has a being so attenuated as to be absolutely incapable of existing apart from some Form ; consequently, without the Form, no Matter.' But Matter was destined to have its revenge. Gassendi's atomic theory seemed completely to reverse the relation. With a slight change of wording, Lucretius's lines expressed the new standpoint :

' Natura videtur
Ipsa sua per se sponte omnia dis agere expers.'

' *Matter* is seen to do all things spontaneously, of herself, *without the Forms.*' Thus Gassendi says : ' The Forms come and go, spring into being and pass away ; . . . but meanwhile matter itself remains uncorrupted, and older than all things which are made, no less in bulk than it was in the beginning, and, as it existed before all the forms, so is it joined to them and survives them.'[1] In his chapter ' On the Birth and Decay of Things,' Gassendi sets out to prove that the generation and decay of all things takes place, not by the addition or loss of some new ' Substance ' called ' a Form,' but by the union or separation or fresh arrangement of the atoms. Forcibly

---

[1] ' Syntagma,' vol. i., p. 232.

he criticizes the Scholastic theory of a twofold power possessed by Matter in respect to Form, the ' eductive potency' enabling Matter to ' educe ' Form from itself, and the ' receptive potency' enabling it to take on the Form thus educed. Form, he says, can no more be educed from Matter, which, the Scholastics hold, is distinct from Form, and does not actually possess it, than can gold pieces be drawn from a purse where they are not. But the whole Aristotelian conception of Matter is full of difficulties. Aristotle's doctrine that Form itself is the first beginning of motion is only possible if by ' Form ' we understand a contexture of the finest atoms spread through the mass of any body. How can Form, as the Scholastics conceive it, ever originate motion, especially seeing that they hold that Form is educed from Matter, and therefore owes its ' entity ' and whatever energy it has to Matter, which they hold to be merely passive ? Or is the Form to borrow its energy from the qualities of Matter which are also educed, or from the Efficient Cause, which again owes its energies to the Form ? ' The difficulty will always return. How can Matter supply to the Form the energy which Matter itself does not possess ?'[1]

On several counts Gassendi's objections appear un-answerable. In the conflict of atoms *versus* Forms, had then the Forms been completely routed, never to reappear on the field ?

We must first ask, What really was the doctrine of Substantial Forms ? I can only touch briefly on it. It must be looked at, not as perverted and debased by the Scholastics, but in its essential meaning as an attempt of great minds to understand the world we live in, so full of thronging life, with its endless variety both of organisms and of inorganic bodies. For one thing, the doctrine of Forms took the place of our modern classifications accord-ing to genera and species ; but it implied a great deal more than this. If we ask why the infant oak with its two or

[1] ' Animadv.,' vol. i., p. 235.

three leaves does not grow up into an asp, or a rose-tree shoot into a vine, or a young sparrow into a blackbird, these are questions before which Science hangs her head and is dumb. We are confident that no such confusion can occur, but she cannot tell us why we are thus confident. To talk of the different arrangement of atoms or cells in the different seeds or embryos is but to play with the question. We have to leave science and come humbly to metaphysics if we wish to obtain an answer. The great thinkers of the Middle Ages held that the Substantial Form of man or animal or plant is that which gives to it its essential reality, which makes it what it is—a man, a horse, a rose-bush. Moreover, the Substantial Form, by attracting to itself and retaining round it certain accidents, explains individuality, and causes a man or horse or rose-bush to be this man, this horse, this rose-bush, and no other. Thus the Substantial Form is something more essential than the matter forming each organism, which last is all that science can take count of. So, when the Substantial Form of a man, the immortal spirit, has stolen away, nothing has gone which can be weighed or measured, but the essential nature of the human being, all that we mean when we say, ' Our friend who is dead '—all this has departed ; only the husk is left behind.

A very acute and able thinker has recently revived the metaphysics of Aquinas, and has even attempted to bring it into agreement with modern science.[1] Father Harper thus describes the doctrine of Form as held by Aquinas : ' All Forms are either material or spiritual. Material Forms enter into the composition of material substances or bodies ; spiritual Forms either subsist of themselves or qualify spiritual substances. Both classes of Forms are either *substantial* or *accidental*. All bodily substances whatsoever are constituted by their Substantial Form. . . . Spiritual Substantial Forms are pure Intelligences, wholly independent of matter. With one exception, they sub-

[1] ' The Metaphysics of the School,' by Thomas Harper, S.J., vol. ii. (Macmillan, 1881).

sist by themselves, and do not enter into intrinsic union with matter. The one exception is the human soul, which is lowest among spiritual Forms; for, though a spiritual substance, it is created to inform a body.' Substantial Forms attract certain accidents and repel others; thus there is a certain colour of hair or eyes and a certain shape of features which we associate with each individual, and which cannot be alienated from that individual. It is the Substantial Form which appropriates these 'accidental' peculiarities, and reduces them under its own unity.

As to these objects which are fashioned by the hand of man, a mass of clay is said by Aquinas 'to be in potentiality' to the form of the porcelain vase. 'The form of the vase which the craftsman has evolved from the clay, that particular form which he had previously conceived in his mind as its model, is so essentially embedded in the clay that it is absolutely impossible to separate the form of the vase and its matter. Not even an infinite power could give it a separate existence. After a somewhat similar manner are the Substantial Forms of bodies evolved out of the potentiality of matter. . . . They are "immersed in matter," to borrow a favourite expression of Aquinas, so that outside of it they can be nothing. . . . Like as the craftsman produces the vase by working his artistic shape out of the matter, so the First Cause concreates matter with its Forms (since neither can exist separately nor be created separately), while secondary causes in the established order of Nature evolve Forms out of matter by direct operation on the matter already pre-existing.'

How does the doctrine of Forms stand related to such a science as Embryology? Mr. Harper's answer to this question is a suggestive one. The animal life of man, his whole 'vegetative' and 'sensitive life,' is precisely similar to that of a plant or animal. The human soul is not, as most modern medical men hold, united to the embryo from its conception, but ' a series of provisional and progressive

Forms successively actuate it ' during its development ; one Form is successively ' expelled ' by another and higher, until at last it has received its highest organic differentiation ; then, when the animal Form is at last driven out, God introduces the spiritual human Form.

It is the doctrine of the ' eduction ' of bodily Substantial Forms out of the potentiality of matter which Father Harper supposes will harmonize the metaphysics of the School with modern physical science. Thus, to take an illustration from chemistry, when phosphorus, which is one of the elements, is combined in due proportion with oxygen, phosphoric anhydride is obtained. The phosphorus in this process ' is corrupted,' as the metaphysician would say ; in other words, its Substantial Form is displaced to make way for the Form of the new compound. On the other hand, the Form of phosphorus only exists potentially in the phosphates that are so abundant in bones ; but by chemical analysis the phosphorus can be isolated, or (as the Scholastic philosopher would say) ' the Form of phosphorus can be educed out of the potentiality of the matter.'   Again, ' if hydrogen be combined with chlorine, the Forms of both substances recede into the potentiality of the matter, and the Form of hydrochloric acid supervenes.   Hence hydrogen can be corrupted. If, again, you plunge a piece of zinc into sulphuric acid, the hydrogen is liberated, as the physicist would say ; to speak metaphysically, the Form of hydrogen is evolved out of the potentiality of the matter ; hence hydrogen can be generated.   If, then, the Forms of phosphorus and hydrogen can be now educed out of the potentiality of matter, now expelled from the same matter by the introduction of another Form, it follows . . . that God so created the element as that its Form should be evolved out of the potentiality of the matter.'

' Whence comes it,' he asks, ' that, in the instance of mechanical mixtures—in wine and water, for instance, or in the union of oxygen and nitrogen in the common air— each constituent remains with its own properties ; whereas in chemically compound bodies—water, for example, or sulphuric acid—the constituents with their properties are not discernible ? Is this generation of what, to all appearance, is an entirely new substance attributable to the mere contiguity of atoms of different shape, weight, mass, together with the interaction of their respective forces ? Such an answer would not commend itself to the common sense of most men. Therefore,' Harper concludes, ' even if it could be proved that the atomic theory is true, it is at least somewhat premature to assert that it can safely dispense with Substantial Forms.'

Is the atomic (as Harper calls it, ' chemico-atomic ') theory true ? In the first place, he objects to it that it assumes that ' the same body is at one and the same time one complete substance and millions of complete substances, which is not a little inconvenient as an object of thought.' Again, atoms that have a shape must be extended ; but an extended atom is a contradiction in terms. ' Extension implies parts, and that which has parts must be divisible. Moreover, the atomic theory implies that all substances—oxygen and iron, for example —are all equally matter composed of atoms. Why, then, is such a portion of matter oxygen, and such another portion iron ? Because of the difference in the shape, weight, etc., of the atoms forming each, it is replied. We cannot admit this explanation, Harper replies : ' The atoms of oxygen are oxygen ; the atoms of iron, iron. Why is the one an atom of oxygen, the other an atom of iron ? To say that the shape, etc., of the atoms of each constitutes the difference is to put an effect in the place of its cause, for the shape of the atoms follows from the nature of the substance, not the nature from the shape. An ox is not an ox because it has four legs, a head and a tail, and lows ; but it has four legs, a head and a tail, and lows because it is an ox. So, sulphur is not sulphur because it has such or such a crystalline form and a yellow colour, but the particular body has such a form and colour because it is sulphur.'

The Forms of Aquinas, it need hardly be said, answer to the Ideas of Plato. The Platonic Ideas, the idea of goodness or beauty, as well as the idea of a man, an animal, a rose-tree, are real things, existing independently, apart from the objects of sense in which they are manifested. Aristotle, however, refuses to accept this doctrine.[1] Such Ideas, according to him, contribute nothing to the existence of sensible objects, and cannot be the cause of any motion or change in them. Without the help of other agents, the invisible ' Idea ' of a house or ring, he says, will never produce a house or a ring. Nor yet do they help to explain how we know things, since they are not immanent in things. Again, we require to imagine some link between everything and its idea ; for example, between the idea of man and any individual man a ' third man ' is required before we can suppose any relation between the two.

Aristotle therefore concludes that the Idea must be something, not outside things of sense, but within them. Unlike Plato, he gives the name of ' Substance ' to the objects of sense, the concrete things in which the Form is united with matter ; in these alone does true and complete reality exist.

Yet Aristotle is, to some extent, a Realist too : he does not deny the existence of Ideas as a second kind of ' Substance '; he holds that the Ideas exist, not as immaterial patterns of earthly things stored up in the heavens, but as immanent in and spread over all the Individuals of each class of things. Thus, the Idea of a ' man ' has its existence in all men who live ; the Idea of the rose-bush is immanent in all rose-bushes, and so on.

How did Plato mean his doctrine of Ideas to be understood ? Are there Ideas of genera only, or of species as well ? of ' man ' alone, or of different types and characters of men ? Or does the upper world contain spiritual duplicates of every individual or thing on earth ? May not Plato have intended his doctrine of Ideas as a myth or

[1] See his ' Metaphysics.'

parable ? Aristotle's criticism of the Ideas as impotent and inoperative on actual things is justified. Thus, from one wooden pattern of a wheel in the pattern-shop of a foundry thousands of iron wheels may be cast, but only by means of human hands and skill. If the Ideas are conceived as thoughts of God, then only can permanence of type and outgoing formative and life-giving energy be united in them.

Centuries after Aquinas his doctrine of Forms was developed still farther by the brilliant Italian thinker who preceded Gassendi, and who in many ways furnishes an extreme contrast to him. Gassendi's whole course was smooth and prosperous : as he rose in the world, his life became more and more a life of compromise, and, as such lives mostly are, uneventful, monotonous ; for the non-combatant does not secure safety and quiet without paying a certain price. Giordano Bruno, on the other hand, allowed no thought of worldly advancement to influence either his actions or his words ; indeed, no man of ordinary prudence who had written what Bruno had written would have been reckless enough to return to Italy and tempt the tender mercies of the Inquisition. I have spoken already of the excessive caution, not to say insincerity, of Gassendi's references to Copernicus. Bruno, however, expressed in the most outspoken way his complete adherence to the system of Copernicus, and with equal fearlessness he declared his admiration for Luther. In both cases his conduct doubtless hastened the doom which he met at the pile in the Campofiore in Rome in 1600—a doom which, even after the strain of a nine years' imprisonment, he encountered with a spirit so calm and unshaken that he seems to need no pity from us. The inspiration which enabled him to die thus, ringed round with hateful and hating faces, without one soul to think his thoughts, to follow him as guide, to stand by him as friend, must have been strong and deep indeed ; in the ' things which are not seen ' he believed with a daring and passion of faith to which ordinary men can only lift up eyes of wonder. His belief in ' the Divine Idea, the

basis of which,' he says, ' is above Nature,' in a spiritual
Power which is behind all we see, and whose glory the
whole world manifests, burned only the stronger for the
life-long anticipation of martyrdom and during long years
in the dungeons of the Inquisition.

In the controversy of Forms *versus* Atoms, Bruno proved
himself a deeper and more inspired thinker than Gassendi.
He has discussed his subject in a dialogue, published in
London, and written during his stay in England from 1583
to 1585.   Here he was the guest of Fulke Greville and of Sir
Philip Sidney, to whom two of his books are dedicated.
The title of this dialogue[1] may be paraphrased ' On the
Unity of Matter and Cause.'   The Aristotelian notions as
to Form and Matter are, he says, the greatest hindrance
to our reaching the truth.   Immaterial Form and formless Matter are mere abstractions.   The Substantial
Forms of the Aristotelians are as abstract as is their
primary matter.   If you ask them in what consists the
essential being of Socrates, they answer, ' In Socrateity.'
[When Crito asks Socrates how he wishes to be buried,
and Socrates replies, ' You may bury me in any way you
like ; only you must catch me first and see that I do not
run away from you '—imagine our substituting for the
spirit of Socrates ' Socrateity ' here !]   If you ask next,
' What do you mean by Socrateity ?' they answer, ' The
proper Substantial Form and proper Matter of Socrates.'
Then, if you set aside this substance in so far as it is
material, and ask, ' What is the substance in so far as it
is Form ?' some of them answer, ' His soul.'   If you ask
next what this soul is, they reply either, ' It is an " ente-
lechy "—that is to say, ' a perfection of the body which
enables it to live,' in which case they represent the soul as
an accident of the body ; or else they reply, ' It is a principle of life, sense, intellect,' but still always assume the
body as the ground of it, and, though calling it a ' principle,' never treat it as a substance.   In short, the

[1] ' Della Causa, Principio ed Uno,' Venice (the nominal place
of publication), 1584.   The scene of the dialogue is laid in London.

Aristotelians never regard the soul as anything but a condition of the body. Their confusion is still more evident if you ask them, ' What is the substantial form of an inanimate thing like wood ?' They answer, ' Ligneity,' but always explain this, taken apart from the matter implied in it, as a mere accident. Thus they have Substantial Forms, but have nothing in Nature which answers to them, so that ' at last they place a mere logical intention as the principle of natural things.'

Bruno will not hear of a dualism of Matter and Form. The Form of every organic being he holds to be identical, not only with the matter composing it, but also with its efficient cause and its final cause.

Space will allow us to quote only two short passages. One of these describes the method of Nature as an evolution from within. Not even a Tyndall, with all the light of modern science, realizes this more keenly than does Bruno. The efficient cause of all things, Bruno holds, is ' the universal Intellect which is the primary and principal faculty of the Soul of the world, that soul being the universal form of this Intellect.' (The Soul of the world we name God.) This universal Intellect ' fills the great whole, enlightens the universe, and instructs Nature how to accomplish her works in the manner most suitable.' The Platonists call it the Demiourgos, but Bruno prefers to call it ' " the inward Artificer," because it fashions matter and shape from within ; from within the seed or the root it sends forth and unfolds the stem ; from within the stem it forces out the boughs ; from within the boughs it pushes out the buds ; from within it forms, shapes and interlaces as with nerves the leaves, the flowers, the fruits ; and from within at appointed times it recalls its own moisture from the leaves and fruits to the branches, from the branches to the boughs, from the boughs to the stem, from the stem to the root.' And there is a like method in the production of animals. If we, by working on the surface of matter from without, can by chiselling and carving produce our own works of art, how much greater an Artificer is that who causes Nature to work, so to say, out of the centre of its substance, formless matter !

Into what a gulf of absurdity, Bruno continues, does Aristotle fall when he asserts that Matter is only a potency, that it has no actual existence until it has taken on a Form, that individual objects, therefore—the table, the tree, the horse—are substances, but that the matter of Nature is not truly a substance.   Matter only a potency ! Fleeting ' Form which,' as Bruno says, ' does but float to and fro on the surface of things ' more real than Matter ! How can we conceive of this ?   Aristotle asserts that the Forms spring from the inward potency of Matter, and are not begotten in it from without.   And rightly so.   Yet all the while he conceives that Matter has no actual existence.   How reconcile these two notions !   No !   Matter is not that *prope nihil*, not that naked, mere empty potency without actuality, energy, and completeness which the modern Aristotelians conceive it ; nor yet is it merely recipient, merely the feminine element, as it were, ever craving to receive new Forms, and never satisfied with receiving Forms enough.   Matter is not void of Forms, but carries them all in infinite number within herself, and brings them forth from her own bosom.   Nature produces things, not by subtracting and adding, as human skill does, as when a sculptor carves out a statue, or when the mason and the carpenter construct a house by adding stone to stone and beam to beam.   Nature makes all things by way of separation, of bringing forth, of outflowing.   Since Matter is ever unfolding what it carries within it, we must call it ' a thing Divine, the mother and bringer forth of things in Nature, *yea, and even* in regard to its substance, *the whole of Nature.*'

Wherever Matter is, the Forms are.   Matter and Form, therefore, are one.

How, then, can the Soul of the world be at the same time Principle and Efficient Cause ?   (By *Principle* Bruno means the intrinsic cause of a thing which remains present in it when constituted ; by *Cause* that which is exterior to the thing.)   ' I affirm,' replies Teofilo, ' that this is not inconsistent if we consider that the soul is in the body as the steersman in the ship, which steersman, in so far as he moves along with the ship, forms part of it, but, in so far as he directs and moves it, he cannot be viewed as a part of it, but as a distinct Efficient (*i.e.*, outer agent).   Thus the Soul of the universe, in so far as it animates and informs the universe, is an intrinsic and formal part of it, but in so far as it directs and governs it, is not a part, but holds the place not of principle, but of Cause.'

' It seems to me,' says Bruno, ' that those belittle the Divine goodness and the excellence of that grand living creature and image of the First Principle who refuse to understand or admit that the world, in its different parts, is animated, as if God envied His world, as if the architect did not love his own work—the architect of whom Plato says that he takes pleasure in his handiwork, because of his own likeness which he admired in it.   Of a truth, what thing more beautiful than that universe can present itself to the eyes of Deity ?'

In God, act and potency are the same thing.   He is everywhere all that He can be ; but as a man is that which he can be, but not all which he can be, so the universe is all which it can be only as a whole, but not in its parts.   Thus it is distinct from, and is but a shadow of, the First Form, as the things which we call real in this world are but the shadows of the true realities, the Divine Ideas.   And Bruno goes on to pass into the region of theology, and attributes to the First Form Goodness and Beauty : ' It is all the goodness which can be, all the beauty which can be.'

Bruno's doctrine that God is not only immanent in the universe, in matter and within our souls, the life of our life, but that He is also transcendent, self-determining, and self-conscious distinct from the universe, the fountain from which Nature is but an emanation, deserves to be called one of the chief stages attained in the history of philosophy.

Bruno, as Maurice has pointed out, struck the Scholastics a crushing blow on their weakest point by showing that their Forms were mere abstractions, mere logical intentions, and that such cannot constitute the essential being of things. It will be seen that his own solution of the problem of Matter and Form does on one side involve Pantheism, but Pantheism of no ignoble sort. He would have assented to Tennyson :

'The sun, the moon, the stars, the seas, the hills, and the plains,
Are not these, O soul, the vision of Him who reigns ?'

And he would also have added, with Tennyson :

'Is not the vision He, *though He be not that which He seems* ?

I can refer only in the briefest way to the marvellous thinker who next embraced the doctrine of Forms, enormously developed it, and brought it into touch with the science of his day, and with the science of all later time. I refer to Leibnitz, who, in developing the doctrine of Forms, showed himself, here as elsewhere, never more original than when he borrows the doctrine of another, and at the same time transforms it, solving with strange ease the difficulties which barred the progress of thinkers preceding him. Leibnitz, in his first recoil from Aristotle, was for a time influenced by the Atomists. ' He turned back again,' says Zeller, ' from the atoms to the Substantial Forms of Aristotle in order to produce his Monads from both of these.' Leibnitz himself used to call his Monads ' Formal Atoms ' (*atomes formels*)—that is, atoms endowed with force. His Monads resemble partly Gassendi's atoms, much more the Forms of Aquinas, and still more the Monads of Bruno, who had much in common with Leibnitz. Leibnitz could not accept atomism. He refuses to admit that matter can be composed of a finite number of very small (but not infinitely small) parts. By affirming such a doctrine, he says, we destroy the unity of the world, and make it a mere collection of parts. Such multiplicity could only be real if its units were genuine, and, to be so, each unit must

contain some kind of force or active principle.   Aristotle's
materia prima (*i.e.*, extension and purely passive body)
is to him a thing unthinkable.   Even extension, he
says, implies resistance — a real force counteracted for
the time by other forces.   Every material body must
consist of extension and force of some kind.   Dead matter
without force, soul, living principle of some kind, is a
mere abstraction.   ' *Atoms of matter* ' (*i.e.*, dead matter)
' are contrary to reason,' he says ; ' the real atoms are
atoms of substance ' (*i.e.*, atoms endowed with force).
Thus Leibnitz denied that atoms have extension : his
Monads are only centres of force.   Merz compares
Leibnitz's Monad to a cone standing on its point, which
may extend indefinitely in height and width.[1]   Thus the
Monads have an inner side which opens into the infinite
while existing only as points in the physical world.   Each
Monad is an independent energy working at a given
centre.[2]

The Monads are indivisible, indestructible, simple
substances, without parts, possessing neither extension
nor figure.   He asserts of the Monads that (to use his
phraseology) ' they all possess ideas,' which differ in
degree of obscurity or clearness, the lower Monads, those
of minerals, possessing ' perception ' without consciousness, these Monads being, as it were, in a sleeping state,
while those of plants reach a higher stage, and in living
things this ' perception ' is combined with consciousness.[3]
There is, indeed, an infinite number of degrees among the
Monads, and each Monad may, by its own ' appetition,'
develop and rise to a higher stage.

The Monads are, in short, ' metaphysical atoms,' each

---

[1] ' Leibnitz,' by John Theodore Merz, 1884, p. 140.

[2] Leibnitz, ' Monadologie,' § 18.

[3] Between Gassendi's ' atoms with the rudiments of consciousness ' and ' Monads with ideas '—ideas which are in their lowest
stage unconscious, but which may develop into consciousness—
the journey is a long one.   Gassendi takes the first step, but the
two thinkers are so different that they could not have travelled
far together along the same road.

one of which perceives and ' mirrors,' and in some marvellous way potentially includes and expresses in itself
the whole universe.   It is a doctrine of Leibnitz that
' there is no individual thing which is not to be regarded
as expressing all others.'[1]   In what way, then, is it possible
for a part to express the whole ?   ' The part,' Dr. Latta
explains, ' cannot contain the whole within itself actually
and fully ; . . . it must contain it potentially . . . or by
representation.'   Thus each part ' must be an expression
of the whole . . . and must contain the whole in such a
way that the whole might be unfolded entirely from
within it.'[2]   The Monads are ' living mirrors ' of the whole,
each Monad both differing from every other, and representing a different phase of the universe.   Contrast the
Lucretian atoms, individual, ' strong in their solid single-
ness,' ' utterly void of sensation,' or the isolated purely
mechanical atoms of Gassendi, possessing no power which
is not derived, with these wondrous self-moving energies,
the ' thinking ' Monads, each of which on one side touches
the material world, while on the other side it extends
illimitably into the infinite continent of Divine power !

Zeller asks, ' How did Leibnitz arrive at the conception
of Monads ?' and answers the question thus : ' Everything
which is active is, according to Leibnitz, a simple substance, and every simple substance is continually
active. . . .   The only simple substance and the only
active force which we know from our own experience is
our Soul.   Only after its analogy can we conceive the
Monads : the original elements of all things, the simple
and vigorously active substances, must be intellectual
thinking Beings, must be Souls.   Thus, in place of the
material atoms appear intellectual individuals, in place of
physical points " metaphysical points "; the world which
Descartes and Hobbes had transformed into a vast
machine is viewed by Leibnitz as a thoroughly living
Whole, as an Organism which is composed of countless
thinking and feeling Beings, an Organism in which there

---

[1] Quoted by Latta, ' Leibnitz,' p. 224 (note).   [2] *Ibid.*, p. 33.

is nowhere anything dead and merely material, in which everything is, according to its own proper nature, Life, Soul, Activity.'[1]

Leibnitz's doctrine of Monads may indeed be called the most astounding dream of all the dreams of metaphysics. What wonder that Kant spoke of Leibnitz's universe as ' a kind of enchanted world '![2]

Tennyson speaks in the very spirit of Bruno when he writes that, if we could understand what the flower growing in the cranny is, ' root and all and all in all,' meaning by this not only to know the outward aspect and fashion of its stem, leaves, flowers, which distinguish it from every other plant, nor yet to be able unerringly to identify its genus and species, but if we could know what is the inward essence which makes its actual being and qualities, causing it to choose the colour and fashion of its own lovely garb which no other flower has, to shed into the air around it its own delicious fragrance, to prefer the crevice between the stones to the richer soil of the garden—that something which neither eye nor microscope can discern, which is permanent while successive flowers and leaves wither and the material substance which it draws from earth and air continually changes; if, in short, it were possible for us to know the true ' Form of the flower,' the unseen power deriving from some principle beyond Nature which constitutes its real life, then we should know what God is and what we ourselves are.

It is the poet—a Bruno, a Tennyson—who comes nearest to grasping, not by slow reasoning, but by swift intuition, the individuality of things which images to us their Forms, the essential attributes which characterize each thing apart from all others. Thus Shelley seizes the distinctive character of the skylark ; Chaucer or Burns, the daisy ; Shakespeare, many a type of humanity. This faculty we even venture to call the ' creative,' in that by

[1] ' Geschichte der Deutschen Philosophie,' by Edward Zeller, 1873, pp. 100 and 106.
[2] Rosenkranz, vol. i., p. 521.

copying and combining the poet can, in a sense, create new types of human character which have a certain generic truth as depicting not individuals, but classes of men.

Diderot has said that, if we suppose a quantity of printed type to be shuffled together from infinity, it is ' not only not impossible, but in fact very probable,' that an ' Iliad ' or a ' Henriade ' might be formed ; and Lange, in his ' History of Materialism,' agrees with Diderot's remark.   Some would question the possibility of this on the ground that the working of chance has its own necessities, while purposeful work has also its own laws ; and, even granting infinite time, blind chance would never be able to produce the same results on any extended scale as mind can.   But let us assume that the text of the poem might, after an infinite shuffling of letters, thus be formed.   In that case the words could only be combinations of letters, not symbols of things or of thoughts : no sentence could express either a thought or an emotion.   The chance-born ' Iliad ' could record for us no story of Troy, no anger of Achilles, nor parting of Hector and Andromache, but only how infinite was the jumble which flung the letters together for a moment, to scatter them the next moment.

Again, imagine, or rather ' fancy '—for imagination has its own laws which cannot be done violence to—that by some much more than miraculous chance a world such as our own could have come into being from the mere clashing of atoms during infinite time.   We cannot conceive of such a world lasting for more than a fleeting moment, for the creatures and things on it would be empty of their true essences, of the underlying reality and inner self of each, by which alone it could persist in being. It could only be a phantasmagoria, bearing as much resemblance to the real world as dolls stuffed with saw- dust and moved by clockwork would bear to living men and women.   Only in a bad dream could we mistake such a phantom for the actual world.

After all, is it surprising that the theologians in Gassendi's day should have charged him with holding doctrines irreconcilable with the belief in God and the immortality of the soul ? They saw him, apparently, merely postulate a God and Creator of the atoms at the beginning ; explain life, death, and all the changes of things by the addition or loss of atoms ; do away with the Substantial Forms, and substitute for them *practically* nothing but atomic movements. What wonder that they saw little difference between his standpoint and that of the confessed enemy of religion, Lucretius :

> ' Natura videtur
> Ipsa sua per se sponte omnia dis agere expers.'

' Nature is seen to do all things herself and entirely of her own accord, without help from the gods.' In those days, when science was struggling for life and the Scholastics were perverting the great doctrine of Forms to their own vicious uses as a mere implement for crushing all direct study of Nature, Gassendi may be excused for saying that little would be lost by giving up the belief in Substantial Forms, and he may sneer at the barbarous term (*hæcceitas*) invented by Duns Scotus to denote the ' individuality ' of a creature or thing ; but these distinctions represent something which mankind feels to be even more essential than the matter of which the things themselves are composed. Does not the very jealousy with which those old theologians and philosophers resented any slightest attack on the doctrine of Forms testify to the instinctive belief of humanity that Spirit is more real than Matter ? The doctrine of Forms has in it something vital ; its roots go deep down to the centre of things, and no mechanical explanation of the world, no mere theory of atoms, could avail to sweep it away. It is a rock against which all the navies of materialism will ever be shattered.

CHAPTER III

JEAN-MARIE GUYAU : THE DOCTRINE OF SPONTANEITY-
IN-THINGS

ONE of the most remarkable contributions which France
has made to the history of ancient philosophy is M.
Jean-Marie Guyau's brilliant work, ' La Morale d'Epicure '
(fifth edition, Paris, 1906). This work, first published in
1878, was at once welcomed as important and eminently
fresh in its treatment. Professor Henry Sidgwick calls it
' not only the most ample and appreciative, but also—
in spite of some errors and exaggerations—the most
careful and penetrating account of the ethical system
of Epicurus.' Though at times differing from his view
of its relation to other systems, in dealing with Epicureanism itself, ' M. Guyau,' he says, ' is almost uniformly
instructive as well as trustworthy.'[1] This remarkable
book was produced by a youth of twenty, being the first
half of a treatise crowned by the French Academy in
1874. When we remember this, it is not surprising that
the career of the ' French Spinoza,' as his admirers call
him, ended at thirty-four. We may not be able to follow
him when he lays an entirely new foundation for ethics,

[1] *Mind* for October, 1879. In the course of a long notice the
Athenæum (August 30, 1879) says : ' This work of M. Guyau's is
full of suggestiveness, originality, and value, and is based on a
complete and masterly appreciation of the data existing. . . .
As a study in ancient philosophy, it is in many respects worthy
to take its place beside even such a work as M. Ravaisson's
" Métaphysique d'Aristote." . . . Those interested in the history
of moral philosophy would be ill-advised to overlook it, and no
one can read it without profit.'

and undertakes to transform our whole conception of
Duty so that it shall require ' no mystical imperative ' to
support it, seeing that our life carries its own sense of
obligation, which he expresses in his maxim : ' I can,
therefore I ought.'[1] We cannot but admire him as an
independent, and in many ways a noble thinker. Both
these qualities are seen in this book. Guyau has been
deeply influenced by his early studies in Epicureanism,
but in assimilating certain of its doctrines, he has marvellously transformed them.

M. Guyau has devoted the whole of a masterly and
admirably-written chapter (pp. 71-102), entitled ' Contingency in Nature the Condition of Free-will in Man,' to
a study of the Epicurean doctrine of Free-will and Atomic
Declination. This very important point of Epicurus's
teaching had hitherto been touched on by almost no other
writer. M. Guyau justifies the length at which he has
treated it by pointing out its importance. He speaks of it,
justly we believe, as ' *the central and truly original point of
the Epicurean system*—namely, the relation of Free-will to
Atomic Declination ' ; and again : ' It is with regard to
this point in particular that Epicurus might truthfully
claim to owe his philosophy to himself alone.' This
chapter, which the author considers to be unquestionably
an important contribution to a true understanding of
Epicureanism,[2] is the part of his work which I now propose
to examine. M. Guyau's explanation of the subject is in
several respects a novel one, and is especially so in regard
to one point—viz., his account of Epicurus's teaching as
to Chance, and the very important part which M. Guyau

---

[1] Guyau holds that life carries with it a necessity for action,
for full and intense living. Out of this necessity, styled by him
' fecundity,' a necessity which is something far deeper than the
mere desire for pleasure, morality is to be evolved. ' Duty,' he
says, ' will be reduced to the consciousness of a certain inward
power, by nature superior to all other powers. To feel inwardly
the greatest that one is capable of doing is really the first consciousness of what it is one's duty to do. . . . Instead of saying,
" I must, therefore I can," it is more true to say, " I can, therefore
I must." '   [2] See his note on p. 7.

supposes it to play in the Epicurean philosophy. According to him, Epicurus believed that the element of Chance which we see at work in the world every day is the manifestation and outcome of a principle of ' Spontaneity ' existing in Nature. This ' Spontaneity ' is the consequence of the power of Declination possessed by the atoms. Thus, Epicurus conceived both Free-will in man and the element of Chance in the world around him to be the result of the same power of Atomic Declination in its twofold working. We shall first state M. Guyau's theory, which he develops in a very subtle way, and then attempt to examine it. If his explanation be correct, it works a strange transformation in the accepted notions of Epicurean doctrine, and Epicurus, who is generally held to be a hard and bare materialist, must have attributed to Nature powers which in some respects remind us of the fairy-tales of our childhood, or of the wilder dreams of Pantheism.

Epicurus, says M. Guyau, after having combated the religious idea of Providence or Divine caprice, found himself confronted with the scientific idea of Necessity. Thus his main philosophic aim was to escape from the notion of gods interfering with Nature on the one hand, and to steer clear of the doctrine of Fate on the other. ' It is better,' said Epicurus, ' to believe in the fables of the gods than to be a slave to the fate of the natural philosophers. The myths allow us the hope of bending the gods by honouring them, but we cannot bend Necessity.'

' To imagine the gods above the world,' M. Guyau goes on, ' was to make oneself a slave ; but to explain all things, oneself included, by necessary reasons which exclude our personal Free-will, would be to do still more : it would be to suppress oneself. Absolute power of the gods or absolute power of the eternal laws, this is the alternative, while the impotence of man is the conclusion.' Epicurus was thus placed ' between the gods of Paganism and the Necessity of the Stoics or of the Natural Philosophers.' This was the dilemma which confronted him.

Epicurus was able to solve it only by adopting an

entirely new philosophical position, taking his stand on which he was able to destroy Necessity and the power of the gods at the same time. ' To introduce into phenomena sufficient regularity that miracle may not be able to find place, and sufficient spontaneity that Necessity may no longer have any absolute, primitive, or decisive power—such is the double aim pursued by Epicurus.' How did he succeed in attaining it ?

It is well known that Epicurus solved the difficulty, in a way satisfactory to himself, by assigning to the atoms the power of Declination. But for this power the world could never have come into existence, for otherwise the atoms could never have come into contact and produced the earth or the life upon it. According to Epicurus, it is the same power of spontaneous movement in the atoms of the soul which alone originates and renders possible the Free-will of man. ' If all beings had within themselves naturally, instead of borrowing it from without, a spontaneous power whence their own movements should originate, might one not thus escape from the universal enchainment of cause and effect ? Might not Nature be conceived to be, essentially, at the same time without the gods and without Necessity ?' Thus, ' Democritus and Epicurus are as logical the one as the other : the first, admitting Necessity everywhere in the world, placed it in man also ; the second, admitting Free-will in man, saw himself compelled to introduce an element of contingency into the world too.'

' It is commonly thought,' M. Guyau continues, ' that Contingency, placed by Epicurus at the origin of things, existed, according to him, at the origin alone, and then disappeared in order again to leave room for Necessity. The world once made, the machine once constructed, why should it not go on by itself without any need of henceforth invoking any other force than Necessity ?' The chain of destiny has been broken once, but closes again ring upon ring, and clasps the universe afresh. ' According to this hypothesis Epicurus must have introduced

declination into Nature only as a kind of dialectic ex-
pedient, and immediately made haste to withdraw it.'

This conclusion has been drawn from Lucretius's often-
repeated statements that phenomena take place according
to fixed conditions, and in particular that men, animals,
trees are produced each after their kind from different
germs, developing according to fixed methods. No
organism can be produced at haphazard, without its
proper germ and necessary conditions, for, says M. Guyau,
translating Lucretius, ' each being is produced from fixed
germs which are the object of scientific *certainty* (' seminibus quia certis quidque creatur'). M. Guyau refers
specially to the use of *certus* with reference to organic life,
and continues : ' It is on this use of the word *certus* several
times repeated in reference to the germs of organisms,
that the conclusion has been based that in the Epicurean
system an unalterable fixedness of effect succeeds the
freedom of the first cause, that " [after the world has once
been formed] " this vast universe obeys and will eternally
obey the laws of necessity, and that henceforth declination is incapable to break the enchainment of causes.'[1]

Such a conclusion, however, runs beyond the thought of
Lucretius. ' Would certain philosophers of our own day
who, like Epicurus, admit—rightly or wrongly—contingency in the universe, believe on that account that an
apple-tree may produce an orange, or an orange-tree an
apple ?' . . . ' It is one thing to believe that the universe,
in its first principles, is not submitted to an absolute
necessity, and another thing to believe in the sudden
derangement of all natural laws or results. The spontaneous and initial movement cannot be calculated and
determined beforehand (" nec ratione[2] loci certa "), but the

[1] The confusion of ideas implied in this paragraph is remarkable. See below, § 2, p. 61. (Of course, *certus* means much
more than ' what is known with scientific certainty.')

[2] Here and at p. 78 M. Guyau reads by some strange mistake
ratione instead of *regione* in the line :

' Nec regione loci certa nec tempore certo.'
ii. 293.

combinations of movements once produced can be calculated and determined ; they constitute a fixed material
which things require in order to come into existence
(" materies *certa* rebus gignundis ").'   It is not true that
Epicurus supposes Declination to disappear from the
world after it has been formed, and henceforth to cease to
exist in it.   He holds the very reverse of this.   ' Wherever
the Epicureans speak of Declination, they consider it not
as ended and done with, not as mere accident, a fortuitous
exception to the order of things occurring once and never
to be reproduced, but as a very real power which both the
atoms and the individuals formed from the union of these
atoms still retain.'

Man calls this power into use every day, nor does it
exist in man alone, but in all forms of matter. M. Guyau
quotes the famous passage on Declination as the origin
of our Free-will, and continues : ' Another passage relating
not now to the declination of souls, but to that of heavy
bodies (" non plus à la déclinaison des âmes mais à celle des
corps pesants ") is no less decisive. Evidently, says
Lucretius, the heavy bodies which we see falling do not in
their descent follow an oblique direction, but " who could
distinguish that they absolutely to no extent decline from
the perpendicular,"

> ' Sed nihil omnino recta regione viai
>   Declinare, quis est qui possit cernere sese ?

Thus, following this somewhat simple conception of
Epicurus, even before our eyes, even in the coarsest
aggregations of matter, spontaneity might easily still
retain a place ; it might manifest itself by an actual,
though imperceptible movement, by a disturbance of
which the effect will appear only after centuries.[1] *Every-*

---

[1] Assuming ' Spontaneity ' to be a fact, we take leave to question whether the result of its working would, in consistence with
the Epicurean doctrine as to the action of Declination, always be
so imperceptibly small and slow as M. Guyau supposes. It is a
principle of Mechanics that a very slight force may let loose a
very great one, just as the huge boulder poised on a mountain-

*where, then, where the atom is found, in external objects as
in ourselves, there will exist more or less latent the power of
breaking necessity, and since, outside the atom, there is only
void, nowhere will an absolute necessity reign : the Free-will
which man possesses will exist everywhere in inferior
degrees, but always ready to awake and act.'*

' Can it be said that in placing spontaneity everywhere
Epicurus placed everywhere a kind of miracle, and thus
returned without wishing it to the conception of a marvellous power like that of the gods ?   No ! and Epicurus
always thought himself able to reject the idea of miracle
while at the same time defending the hypothesis of
declination, which was dear to him.   That there may
really be miracle, two conditions must be realized : first,
we must suppose powers existing outside of Nature, then
we must attribute to them a potency over Nature large
enough at once to modify, after a preconceived plan, an
ensemble of phenomena.   On the contrary, the spontaneity of the atoms is a power placed in the things themselves, not outside them, and at the same time this power
is exercised only over a single movement ; it oversteps the
necessary laws of mechanics (ulterior and derivative laws)
only on a single point, and in a quite imperceptible
manner.   Spontaneous movements can have results only
at length, by accumulation, by permitting new combinations, by thus aiding the march of things instead of
hindering it : *spontaneity, if it exists, works to the same
purpose as Nature ;* to believe Epicurus, we do not really
disturb the laws of Nature when, by a decision of the will
impossible to determine, we resolve in such or such a way,
or take such and such a direction.   Miracle, on the contrary, is in direct and formal opposition to Nature ; it is a
violent arrest of the march of things. . . . *Spontaneity, on*

---

ledge may be finally cast down by some tiny rush of water.   The
spontaneous movement of a mass of matter, however slight, might
still be able to give the initial impulse required to let loose a
mighty force.   Thus, ' Spontaneity ' might easily produce important results in Nature.

the contrary, precedes, follows, and completes Nature, hinders
it from being a pure mechanism incapable of improvement ;
it is for this that Epicurus maintains it ; he hopes, rightly
or wrongly, thus to counterbalance necessity, yet without
disturbing the order of things ' (pp. 91, 92).

Fragments of Epicurus's own writings and the statements of ancient writers show, says M. Guyau, that
Epicurus believed ' Chance ' or ' Fortune ' to play a very
important part in the world. ' Those external events
which are not originally submitted to a necessary law, but
to spontaneous causes, the effects of which we cannot
foresee, are referred to Chance.' Epicurus believed this
principle of Chance or Accident which we see at work
every day around us to be the manifestation and
outcome of the power of Spontaneity which resides in
Matter.

' Chance does not mean for Epicurus the absence of
cause : for we know nothing is done without cause,
nothing comes from nothing ; it is on this very principle
that Epicurus rests in order to induce our Free-will on
Nature. Nor yet is Chance, as has been often said, the
same as Free-will, for Epicurus always places the two
terms, chance and liberty, parallel, without confounding
the one with the other (ἃ μὲν ἀπὸ τύχης, ἃ δὲ παρ᾽ ἡμᾶς).
Chance, in fact, is exterior, liberty is interior.' ' Chance
is a manner in which things appear in their relation to
us ; it is the unforeseen, the undeterminable, which occurs
at an uncertain time and place. *But this element of the*
unforeseen is the result of a cause which hides itself behind
Chance. This cause . . . is, in fact, as we have seen, *the*
spontaneity of motion inherent in the atoms. Chance is
only the form under which this spontaneity reveals itself
to us.' This, says M. Guyau, completely explains the
passage of Plutarch which we can now better understand :
' Epicurus assigns the power of declination to the atoms
. . . in order that Chance (τύχη) may be produced, and
that Free-will (τὸ ἐφ᾽ ἡμῖν) may not be destroyed.' ' Τύχη
and τὸ ἐφ᾽ ἡμῖν *are the two modes of a spontaneity identical*

at bottom, to which Epicurus has just told us[1] that the
destiny of the natural philosophers is reduced.'

All this has a practical bearing on man's life in the
world. This external Chance when once manifested
becomes a power more or less hostile to us—Fortune.
' Fortune, it is true, is no longer a power absolutely
invariable and unconquerable as destiny was. With
changing and variable Chance, hope is always permitted—
nay, more, always enjoined. . . . Since no inflexible
destiny can now impose itself upon us either without or
within, Nature cannot have dominion over us ; we, on the
contrary, ought to command her by our Will.   The wise
man who might have been reduced to despair and helpless-
ness before the Absolute of necessity or of Divine caprice
will recover all his strength when confronted with Chance
—that is to say, at bottom, with Spontaneity—that is,
with a power which is no longer terrible like the unknown,
but which he knows—nay, more, which he carries within
himself. He will then stand up like a wrestler against
Chance, and will struggle with it hand to hand—a noble
contest, in which the wise man sure of his superior liberty
is sure of his final triumph.' Thus, according to M.
Guyau, in the struggle of man with Nature, seeing that
man has a high degree of Spontaneity and also Life and
consciousness, while he fights against things which
possess Spontaneity only without life, man has an
enormous advantage.

M. Guyau has now conducted us to the moral bearing
of the question. He has shown how the Epicurean wise
man need not tremble at Fortune with her turning-wheel.
' Fortune or Chance has so little empire over the wise man
that it is better,' said Epicurus, ' to be unfortunate
according to reason than to be fortunate without reason.'
In conclusion, he points out (pp. 99-102) ' the close
solidarity established between man and the world which

---

[1] Epicurus merely says (Diog. L., x. 133) that instead of
Necessity being the mistress of all things, events are in reality
due partly to Chance and partly to our own Free-will.

the doctrine implies.' ' Nature and man,' as he has before
said, ' are so *solidaires* that we cannot find anything absolutely new in the one which should be wanting in the
other : if we wish to recognize a principle of Spontaneity
and liberty in ourselves, do not let us entirely withdraw it
from things. We cannot set limits to Necessity and say,
It reigns all around us, but it does not reign over us.'
' We naturally imagine that the whole universe may be
subjected to Fate, without our Free-will, if it does exist,
receiving any prejudice from it. But, then, asks Epicurus, whence could this Free-will come ? (" Unde est hæc,
fatis avolsa, potestas ?") how could it be born and subsist
in a world absolutely under the sway of necessary laws ?
. . . No, all causes are natural, and since " nothing comes
from nothing," our Free-will comes from Nature itself.
It is curious to see Lucretius thus invoking in favour of
Spontaneous Declination the famous axiom *ex nihilo
nihil*, which has so often been urged precisely against this
hypothesis.' According to Lucretius, what is in the effect
exists already in the causes ; if we can move at will, ' all
the parts of our being which, by gathering together,
have formed us, must possess an analogous power,
more or less extensive, more or less conscious [! *cf.*
Lucr., ii. 972, " primordia . . . haut ullo prædita sensu "],[1]
but real.'

' The adversaries of Epicurus attempted, as we have
seen,[2] to escape from the dilemma which he laid down for
them—either spontaneity in things or necessity in the
soul—but it is doubtful whether they succeeded. In our

[1] Or ii. 990 : ' Seminibus . . . carentibus undique sensu.'
[2] M. Guyau refers to the ingenious argument of Carneades,
who taught that declination was unnecessary, since both the
atoms and man have power to move without any external cause
in virtue of their own *nature* (' Ipsius individui hanc esse naturam,
ut pendere et gravitate moveatur, eamque ipsam esse causam
cur ita feratur . . . similiter ad animorum motus voluntarios non
est requirenda externa causa ; motus enim voluntarius eam
naturam in se ipse continet ut sit in nostra potestate, nobisque
pareat, nec id sine causa, eius enim rei causa ipsa natura est.'—
Cicero, ' De Fato,' xi.).

own day the same dilemma still meets us. . . .   Let there
be a single being, a single molecule, a single atom in the
universe in which spontaneity does not exist, and beyond
doubt Free-will will no longer be able to find place within
us ; all existing things are *solidaire*.   Inversely, if Free-
will exists in man, it cannot be absolutely foreign to
Nature.'   ' Hypothesis for hypothesis, we a hundred times
prefer the Epicurean *clinamen* to the vulgar doctrine of
Free-will restricted to man.'

M. Guyau does not examine how far ' this universal
spontaneity, this element of variability introduced into
the universe, may agree with the theories of modern
science as to the equivalence of forces and the mechanical
laws of evolution.'   His task has been ' simply to look for
the true meaning, and to show the historical importance
of one of the chief theories of Epicurus.'

Most students of ancient philosophy will be astonished
at the entirely new light which this chapter of M. Guyau's
pours over Epicureanism.   So reasonable and consistent
with the logical results of some part of Epicurean doctrine
is his explanation, so forcibly does he grasp and express it,
and so skilfully does he handle and combine the evidence
which seems to support his opinion, that we seem at first
compelled to admit its historic accuracy.   And if so, must
not Epicureanism be the very reverse of what it has been
thought ?   How much of the marvellous it must have
included !   If ' Spontaneity ' exist even in brute-masses
of matter, if the stone which I hold in my hand—not
merely its individual atoms, as Epicurus did indubitably
assert, but if the mass of stone itself possess ' Spontaneity ' and Will so that it can move in any direction at
pleasure, what matter though its movements be so slight
as to be imperceptible to the human eye—does not this
remind us of those fairy-tales, which show how in simpler
ages than this men found it easy to credit all sorts of
magical powers in Matter, and looked upon all objects of
the outer world as animated with a life resembling their

own ?[1] This tendency is seen in such stories as that of the rocks which the early Greek mariners believed had the habit of dashing together so as to crush unwary ships ; of the good ship *Argo*, which has sunk so deep into the sand that she cannot be launched, but when the prophet sings to his lyre, she rises out of her sandy bed, and rushes forward into the sea ; of the granite boulders which, as the French peasant believes, can leave their places on the heath by night, and thunder heavily after the belated traveller ; of the automatic cudgel which can beat a man at its owner's bidding, or a hundred others. We are ever reminded of Hans Andersen's delightful stories, where everything in the world, from the Fir-tree, the Rose-bush, and the Daisy, down to the Old Lamp and the Silver Shilling, possesses personality and consciousness each after its own degree and kind. True, Epicurus asserted for his atoms, and, according to M. Guyau, also for masses of matter in every form, *Will* and consequent power of motion *without Life* and consciousness. But the common mind is utterly incapable of drawing such a distinction, and where Will is, it must without fail conceive Life and all its attributes to be also. ' Everywhere where the atom is, in external objects as well as in ourselves, will exist more or less latent the power of breaking necessity.' . . . ' The Free-will which man possesses will exist everywhere in inferior degrees, but always ready to awake and act.' . . . The atoms which have formed our bodies must possess a power of Free-will ' analogous to our own, more or less extensive, more or less conscious, but real.' And if this ' Spontaneity '

[1] Comte has described this under the name of ' Fetichism,' as a necessary stage of human development. It is the tendency of man, as seen in the history of every race, to look upon the world around him as animated like himself in greater or less degree. Comte's language on this subject strikingly reminds us of M. Guyau's description of ' Spontaneity '—' Pur fétichisme constamment charactérisé par l'essor libre et direct de tendance primitive à concevoir tous les corps extérieurs quelconques, naturels ou artificiels, comme animés d'une vie essentiellement analogue à la nôtre avec des simples différences mutuelles d'intensité ' (' Philosophie Positive,' vol. v., p. 30).

residing in what we call dead Matter has such power as to produce the fortuitous and unexpected in Circumstance, that which we cannot calculate upon, and which happens at times and in places where we do not look for it, either coming to baffle us or bringing us success, so that what we call ' Chance ' in the affairs of daily life is the direct result of the long-continued blind-working of ' Spontaneity ' in Matter, does not a conception like this bring us nearer to the world of Fairy-tale than to that of Science, still less to that of Materialism ?   What strange results might come of such a potency in Matter !   One cannot help thinking how a power like this, were it possible for it to exist in a world such as ours and under the domain of natural law, would in many ways render Nature far more terrible to man than she is.   How easily might such a force set the avalanche sliding on the mountain-side, or bring down the hanging rock upon the passer-by, or set the tempest brewing, or waken the fires hidden below the volcano from their uneasy sleep.   What wild terrors might storm, flood, and earthquake become were they to be aided by a power like this !   And in all cases ' Spontaneity ' would be the more dangerous, since, unlike the other forces of Nature, it has no fixed methods, but manifests itself

> ' Incerto tempoɪe ferme
> Incertisque locis '

(' at quite uncertain times and uncertain spots '), so that we cannot forecast its working.   But it is now full time to examine M. Guyau's evidence.   Is his explanation of this important Epicurean doctrine historically accurate, or is it not ?

1. How does M. Guyau reconcile the existence of ' Spontaneity ' in things with the leading Epicurean principle of the constancy of natural laws, a principle which we have shown was grasped as strongly by Lucretius as it is by any modern man of science ?

2. In the first place, M. Guyau appears to us never fully to realize or give account to Epicurus's distinct and

decided grasp of the fact of Law in Nature. Indeed, he appears actually to contradict it. He objects (pp. 87-89) to our supposing that, according to Epicurus, ' contingency existed solely at the origin of things, and afterwards disappeared in order again to make way for necessity,' and that ' this universe now obeys, and will obey, eternally the laws of necessity, and that declination is henceforth unable to break the enchainment of causes.' This part of M. Guyau's chapter involves a rather intricate confusion of ideas, and is in one respect entirely false. According to Lucretius and his Master, Law reigns everywhere in Nature, and ' Necessity ' is a name given by both[1] to the order of Nature resulting from natural law, though Lucretius[2] uses the word in this sense comparatively

---

[1] Epicureans would probably have assigned the movements of the heavenly bodies as the readiest instance of that which has ' Necessity ' for its cause. Epicurus does so in his letters (Diogenes Laertius, x. 77 and 113), and similarly he speaks of Necessity (ἀνάγκη) as a possible First Cause of the movement of the heaven or of the stars (*ibid.*, x. 92 : κατὰ τὴν ἐξ ἀρχῆς ἐν τῇ τοῦ κόσμου γενέσει ἀνάγκην ἀπογεννηθεῖσαν ; *cf.* also x. 93). We may compare καὶ τίσιν ἀνάγκαις ἕκαστα γίγνεται τῶν οὐρανίων (' Memorabilia,' i. 1, 12 ; *cf.* i. 1, 15), where Xenophon uses the word in the precise meaning of ' natural laws.' In the same way Aristotle says that ' great storms and floods recur διὰ χρόνων εἱμαρμένων—*i.e.*, at fixed periods—' just as winter occurs at a given season of the year ' (' Meteor,' i. 14).

[2] As at v. 309, 310 :

> ' Nec sanctum numen *fati* protollere *finis*
> Posse neque adversus naturæ fœdera niti,'

where *fati finis*, ' the limits of fate,' refers to the same thing as *naturæ fœdera*. So the famous passage on Free-will, if correctly understood, distinctly implies that the world outside man is absolutely governed by Fate (*cf.* the context of ii. 254, *fati fœdera* : 257, *fatis avolsa potestas*), and here evidently Lucretius shows that he conceives the laws of Nature as Fate. Occasionally Lucretius uses *vis* in the sense of ' necessity ' instead of *fatum* or *necessum*, as at ii. 289, where *externa vis* is opposed to *necessum intestinum*. The passage vi. 29-32, which touches on the source of evil in human affairs—

> ' Quod fieret *naturali* varieque volaret
> *Seu casu seu vi*, quod sic natura parasset '—

seldom. Lucretius firmly believes that nowhere in
Nature can you escape from law. In this sense Epicureans *did* conceive the world after its origin ' to obey
the laws of necessity,' to be ' subject to an absolute
necessity.'

3. M. Guyau has referred to those passages in which the
word *certus* occurs, and frequently with reference to the
germs of organisms—*e.g.*,

> ' Seminibus quia certis quæque creantur.'
>
> > i. 169.
>
> ' Atque hac re nequeunt ex omnibus omnia gigni,
> Quod certis in rebus inest secreta facultas.'
>
> > i. 172.
>
> > ' Omnia quando
> Paulatim crescunt, ut par est, semine certo.'
>
> > i. 189.
>
> ' Si non materies quia rebus reddita certast
> Gignundis e qua constat quid possit oriri.'[1]
>
> > i. 203.

He might have added many other passages, such as :

> > ' Omnia quando
> *Seminibus certis certa genetrice* creata
> Conservare genus crescentia posse videmus.
> Scilicet id *certa* fieri *ratione* necessust.'
>
> > ii. 707-710.
>
> ' Certum ac dispositumst ubi quicquit crescat et insit.'
>
> > iii. 787.

Cf. also v. 669-679 ; v. 923-924 ; v. 1436-39.

---

seems to mean that it is indifferent whether you call the cause
of evil from one point of view ' natural chance,' seeing that, as
concerns us, it is not fixed or decreed whom it is to injure, or from
another standpoint ' natural necessity,' since, if we come into
collision with it, it will and must, according to Nature's law,
inevitably injure or crush us. The passage, of course, implies
that you must *not* ascribe evils either to Divine Providence or to
Fate. Here *vis naturalis* certainly refers to the ' necessity ' which
is the consequence of natural laws. See also Munro's note on
v. 77, and on vi. 31.

[1] At p. 89 M. Guyau seems to misunderstand this. He renders
' Une matière certaine dont les choses ont besoin pour naître.'
But *materies certa* refers to the atoms and their unchanging

M. Guyau (pp. 88, 89) appears to us considerably to mis-understand the force of *certus* in these passages. It refers to the *fixity* and *unchangeableness* of law as manifested in natural productions. Things which are entirely subject to natural law, such as the growth of trees and plants, and the development of living bodies, animals, and men, each after its kind and from its own proper germ, are ' fixed ' (*certus*) in respect of the time, place, and conditions of their coming into being, and continuing in existence. On the other hand, the will of man is not thus predetermined by causes outside himself ; it acts—

> ' Nec tempore certo
> ' Nec regione loci certa.'

M. Guyau does not by any means sufficiently distinguish between the two Epicurean principles of absolute fixity of law (sometimes in Epicurean language called ' Neces-sity ') in Nature and perfect Spontaneity of Free-will action in man.

4. The question now very naturally occurs to us, If Matter everywhere possesses ' Spontaneity,' and is always exerting it, how can this be without interfering more or less with the constancy of natural law, the principle upon which all Epicurean science was based ? However slight and gradual such declination may be, if all bodies every-where are exerting it, they must, inevitably, more or less disturb the orderly sequence of natural phenomena, if not destroy the conditions under which Law is possible. M. Guyau appears to think that the slightness of the amount of such action (' une perturbation dont l'effet n'apparaîtra qu'après des siècles ') will produce a variation so small and slow as not to interfere with Nature, but as we have already pointed out, if we assume ' Spontaneity ' to be possible, the amount of its action cannot be counted

character. Similarly at p. 69, when M. Guyau translates ' Finita potestas denique cuique Quanam sit ratione,' ' Par quelle raison chaque chose *n'a qu'une puissance limitée*,' he misunderstands *finita* and misses the idea, which is the fixity and definiteness of natural laws. *Cf.* also p. 70.

on.   At one time, its working in some huge mass might be
imperceptibly small ; at another it might chance to be
enough to let loose and set a-going some vast atomic
machinery with far-reaching consequences ; or if it chanced
to combine with a series of other spontaneous movements
in other bodies and from other sources, its results might be
enormous and speedy enough.   In any case, however, if such
a power be exerted by Matter, there can be no fixed laws
of Nature, no *fœdera certa*, no *terminus alte hærens*.   A far
less shrewd thinker than Epicurus could hardly have failed
to see that ' Spontaneity ' in the various forms of Matter
cannot exist side by side with absolute laws of Nature.

5. M. Guyau has foreseen this, and tries to guard
against it by assuming that ' Spontaneity ' cannot disturb
natural order, because it works in harmony with Nature
(' va dans le sens de la nature ').   The assumption is
baseless, and rather a bold one.   Why should not ' Spontaneity ' as well work *against* natural order ?

6. But supposing atoms to possess the power of movement in any direction at will, does it follow that any body
formed out of atoms—say a mass of stone—can *as a body*
possess the same power of movement which its atoms have
as atoms ?   Certainly not, according to Epicurus's conception of the atoms ; rather would one of its component
atoms move in one direction, another in an opposite, and
thus they would counteract each other, and the body
remain inert.   M. Guyau (quoted above at p. 54) states
that one passage (ii. 249, 250) decisively shows that
Lucretius believed in ' the declination of heavy bodies ' as
well as in ' the declination of minds.'   But M. Guyau has
entirely misunderstood the passage in question :

' Quare etiam atque etiam paulum inclinare necessest
Corpora ; nec plus quam minimum—*ne fingere motus
Obliquos videamur et id res vera refutet.*
Namque hoc in promptu manifestumque esse videmus,
Pondera, quantum in sest, non posse obliqua meare,
Ex supero cum præcipitant, quod cernere possis ;
*Sed nil omnino recta regione viai
Declinare quis est qui possit cernere sese ?*'
　　　　　　　　　　　　　　　　　　ii. 243-250.

This passage comes in such a connection as to be most easily misunderstood, especially by those unfamiliar with Epicurean logic. At first and even second reading it certainly appears, especially if, with Guyau (p. 91) and Giussani (p. 102), we detach from it the first three lines, to bear the meaning which M. Guyau has given it. Taken in its context, it amounts to this : ' We never see falling bodies swerve, it is true,' says Lucretius, ' but that does not prove it to be against Nature, and impossible for such a thing to happen. The human eye is incapable of deciding that falling bodies move in an *absolutely straight* line. A stone falling to the ground may slant to an exceedingly small extent for all that we can tell. Therefore, *so far as the evidence of sense is concerned*, it is not impossible that the atom should swerve (" nec plus quam minimum ") to a very slight extent.' It is well known what stress Epicurus laid on the principle that the senses cannot deceive, and it is the apparent testimony of sense, of observed facts (' res vera '), which Lucretius is combating in these two lines.

7. When Lucretius says that it is not impossible that falling bodies may swerve, we might naturally assume that he believes they do, and ask next : ' Why do such masses swerve ?' As to this Lucretius says nothing. He has before asserted that we believe the atoms to fall vertically because we *see* bodies fall vertically. He is now anxious to assert that the all-important evidence of sense does not contradict an imperceptible swerving of the atoms. We can infer nothing more from these two lines. We have no right to assume that Epicurus and Lucretius held that the swerving of single atoms has the power to give masses of matter a potency of corporate movement. This is merely an ingenious but very uncritical inference.

Giussani, who adopts Guyau's theory and expounds it at great length, refers to this passage as proving that Epicurus ' admits a certain spontaneity in created Nature manifested in things which do not possess Free-will.' . . . ' The argument of these lines could not have any value if it were not implied in it that, according to Epicurus, some bodies, such as stones, falling and deflected by no force, may deviate, and at times do deviate, spontaneously.' . . . ' The possible eventual declination of bodies perceptible by sense proves the possible eventual declination of the atoms.' . . . ' And here (let it be said in passing) is a new argument against the principle " non plus semel atomum declinare," since the declination of a stone can result only from the declination of the atoms or of its own atoms.'[1]

Giussani here assumes far too much. It is a specialty of Epicurean logic that it presses the absence of arguments to the contrary as positive proof of a proposition. Such a negative proof we have here in ll. 249, 250. Here Lucretius says merely οὐκ ἀντιμαρτυρεῖται (see Diog. L., x., § 33; Sextus Empir., i. 210 ff.). According to both grammar and logic, the words might bear the meaning supposed. Yet the brief reference is purely controversial, and does not amount to an assertion of the proposition that masses of matter can decline. Lucretius refers merely to the evidence of sense, and does not need to go further.

Giussani continues : ' We have here a declination in material objects existing in the world,[2] which stands midway between the primeval declination of the isolated atoms and voluntary declination [of living creatures] ; hence we have a gradation corresponding to the gradation of facts relatively to their causes, as referred to by Sextus Empiricus and to the gradation of Epicurus himself in the passage cited in the preceding note.'[3]

In these passages Giussani adopts and expands Guyau's theory of a ' threefold declination,' mounting gradually upwards, from the blind swerving of single isolated atoms in the void to the ' spontaneity ' of unconscious masses of matter, and culminating in conscious human volition.

8. The passage of Lucretius above discussed is M.

---

[1] ' Studi Lucreziani,' p. 153.

[2] Literally, ' in full created Nature (in piena natura creata)'.

[3] These passages (Sextus Empir., p. 736; and Diog. L., x. 133) are discussed in the note on § 9.

Guyau's main evidence for the assertion that, according
to Epicurean belief, masses of matter have the power to
decline as well as atoms. What other proof does he bring
forward ? Out of all the authorities quoted, only one
passage from Plutarch contains anything at all distinct
enough to appear to support M. Guyau's theory, but so
skilfully does he lead up to his conclusion that the evidence seems stronger than it is. Indeed, the passages
referred to bear only in the vaguest way on the present
subject. They simply assert that Epicurus often attributed events to Fortune. But most ancient philosophers
speak in the same way, and assign more or less power to
Fortune in ordering what comes to pass. M. Guyau
quotes one passage of Plutarch, translating it as follows :
' Epicurus assigns declination to the atom . . . in order
that chance may be produced and free-will may not be
destroyed : ἄτομον παρεγκλῖναι ("spontaneity of declination ") . . . ὅπως τύχη παρεισέλθῃ ("external chance which
is the form of it "), καὶ τὸ ἐφ' ἡμῖν μὴ ἀπόληται ("inward
liberty which is the feeling of it ").' This commentary
builds a good deal on Plutarch's accidental and sarcastic
reference to Epicurus, even were the sentence exactly as
M. Guyau has quoted it. Plutarch does not refer to
Epicurus at all in the context, but simply makes a fling at
him in passing, as follows :

' The philosophers do not allow Epicurus, even in order
to account for the greatest things, to assume so small and
unimportant a matter as the least possible declination of
a single atom,[1] in order that the worlds and living
creatures and Fortune may be smuggled in,[2] and that our
Free-will may not be destroyed.'

In the next sentence Plutarch passes on to a quite
different subject. Instead of saying that Epicurus intro-

[1] Plutarch, ' De Solertia Animalium,' chap. vii. Probably the
words ἄτομον παρεγκλῖναι μίαν are not intended to be understood
literally in the sense that Epicurus required the declination of ' a
single atom ' only to begin with.

[2] ὅπως ἄστρα καὶ ζῶα καὶ τύχη παρεισέλθῃ, ' may slip in at the
side.' The word is used sarcastically.

duced the doctrine of Atomic Declination principally or
solely to account for Chance, as M. Guyau's quotation
would certainly make us suppose, Plutarch is stating
correctly enough the general objects which Epicurus
thought to effect by Declination—viz., to allow the origin
of the worlds and of man, and to render Free-will possible
(ὅπως . . . τύχη παρεισέλθῃ meaning simply ' to get rid of
Necessity ').

9. There is no doubt that the Epicurean writers spoke
much of Chance. In the Epicurean system, which
rejected all and any Providence, Chance must from the
very facts of human nature have come to be an important
item in everyday calculations about human affairs.
Epicureans refused to own any Divine agency in the world,
but practically they had set up a new Divinity, Chance,
which was for them a real enough one. Chance must
have been often in the mouth of an Epicurean,[1] just as
naturally as Providence was in that of a Stoic, or ' the
hand of God ' in that of a Puritan. It was simply natural
that Lucretius should pray that the abstraction *Fortuna
gubernans* might avert the end of the world.

Lucretius not merely opposed the notion of Gods from
time to time interfering with Nature, but he, like other
Epicureans, would have combated with equal ardour the
belief, held in a very noble form by the Stoics, in a universal Providence ordaining each and every event of
human life, as well as maintaining all the ongoings of
Nature. Such a conception would have appeared to
him only another form of Necessity, and almost equally
objectionable. In human affairs Providence (according to

---

[1] *Cf.* the opinion ascribed by Hippolytus (' Ref. Hær.,' i. 22)
to Epicurus : ὅλως πρόνοιαν μὴ εἶναι μηδὲ εἱμαρμένην ἀλλὰ πάντα
κατὰ αὐτοματισμὸν γίνεσθαι—' There is neither Providence at all,
nor yet Destiny, but all things take place by Chance,' or ' happen
of themselves.' As the Lucretian parallel for πάντα κατὰ αὐτοματισμὸν γίνεσθαι, we might quote :

' *Natura videtur*
Ipsa sua per se sponte omnia dis *agere* expers.'
ii. 1090-92.

the Pagan notion of it, as represented by Virgil's gods and
goddesses, who bitterly persecute the human beings who
have unwittingly and often innocently given them offence)
had come to be dreaded. Chance seemed less formidable.

It is very difficult for us, accustomed to modern phraseology, to understand the exact meaning of such words
as Chance and Necessity in the Epicurean as also in
other systems of ancient philosophy. For example,
Stobæus (i. 206) tells us that 'Epicurus distinguishes
among Causes that by Necessity, that by Free-will, and
that by Fortune'—Ἐπίκουρος (προσδιαρθροῖ ταῖς αἰτίαις
τὴν) κατ' ἀνάγκην, κατὰ προαίρεσιν, κατὰ τύχην.[1] Perhaps

---

[1] The question, 'Is Fortune a Cause?' was often debated in
the schools of Greece.

Aetius, in his section περὶ τύχης ('De Plac. Phil.,' i. 29),
followed by Stobæus (i. 218), asserts that Epicurus held Fortune
to be ἀσύστατον αἰτίαν—'an unstable cause operating in respect
of persons, times, and places.' The expression may be Epicurus's
own or not. The other passage referred to by Giussani as proving
that Declination is 'threefold' is at Diog. L., x. 133, where
Giussani adopts the text of Usener, who inserts more than a line
of Greek to improve the sense : τινα νομίζεις κρείττονα εἶναι τοῦ
. . . τὴν ὑπό τινων δεσπότιν εἰσαγομένην πάντων διαγελῶντος
[εἱμαρμένην καὶ μᾶλλον ἃ μὲν κατ' ἀνάγκην γίγνεσθαι λέγοντος],
ἃ δὲ (μὲν manuscripts) ἀπὸ τύχης, ἃ δὲ παρ' ἡμᾶς. Usener makes
Epicurus here assert a threefold cause of events : 'Whom can
you think better than the man who . . . scorns to believe in
Fate, whom some set up as the mistress of all things, but instead
of this refers some things to Necessity, and others to Fortune, and
others to our own Free-will?' The addition is ingenious, and
may be true, yet has only the authority of a conjecture. Probably all the passage needs is to understand καὶ λέγοντος.

At § 134 Epicurus goes on to say that Fortune is neither θεὸν
nor yet αἰτίαν : she does not give us either good or evil, but
only puts to our hand the 'beginnings' or 'opportunities'
(ἀρχὰς) of either.

Guyau, followed by Giussani, quotes as a doctrine of Epicurus
the sentence : τὰ μὲν τῶν γινομένων κατ' ἀνάγκην γίνεται, τὰ δὲ
κατὰ τύχην τὰ δὲ παρ' ἡμᾶς (Sextus Empir., p. 736, ed. Bekker,
1842). But Sextus does not name or refer to Epicurus either here
or in the context. The only ground for assigning these words to
Epicurus is that Stobæus, on the subject of 'Causes,' sums up
Epicurus's view in the rough jotting quoted above to the same
effect as Sextus's sentence ('Ecl. Phys.,' i. 206).

we may best explain this by taking an instance, such as
the incident used as an illustration by Lucretius, of the
Roman admiral and his fleet destroyed by the tempest.
Here there would be, according to the phraseology just
quoted, three ' Causes ' at work : (1) ' Necessity,' or, as
Lucretius once calls it, *vis naturalis*, ' natural Necessity '
—*i.e.*, the laws which produce storms, and which cannot
do otherwise than produce them at their given time and
place (' certo tempore, certo spatio '). At the present day
we should call this, far more appropriately, Natural Law.[1]
(2) Free-will, which works ' incerto tempore ferme In-
certisque locis.' The admiral was free to have taken
another course, or to have delayed his voyage till a safer
time, but he chose to sail then and in the direction where
the tempest was to burst. (3) Chance—that is to say,
the way in which the forces of Nature, in their working,
bear on man. It might easily have been otherwise.
The storm might have raged either sooner or later,
or over another portion of the sea, but as it coin-
cided with the course and the time which the admiral
chose, Nature could do nothing else than destroy him.
Chance comes into play where the forces of Nature
come to bear for good or evil on human affairs.[2]
These three principles do not by any means stand in
the same category. ' Necessity ' and Free-will are both
causes, but Fortune is in no sense a cause, and can

---

[1] See notes on § 2, pp. 75, 76. Epicurus boasted that he
had cast out Necessity from the moral world. Here he claimed
to have substituted for it the two notions of Chance and Free-
will (Diog. L., x. 133). He still called the laws of Nature, in
so far as they absolutely govern the world outside man, ' Necessity,' but in the physical world also the principle of Law which
he had done so much to establish was really destined to substitute
for the notion of Necessity a higher idea, though neither Epicurus
nor Lucretius had any anticipation of this.

[2] The words ἀνάγκη and τὸ αὐτόματον occur in somewhat
strange collocation in the interesting fragment published by
Gomperz (' Neue Bruchstücke Epikur's,' 1876, pp. 8-11), ἐν τῇ
τοῦ περιέχοντος καὶ ἐπεισιόντος κατὰ τὸ αὐτόματον ἀνάγκη. Here
Epicurus is evidently defending the freedom of the mental processes in reference to his theory of Perception by Images.

only be called so by a popular and unscientific use of language.

10. While for the reasons given we cannot allow that M. Guyau's theory of ' Spontaneity ' is correct, or that there is evidence to prove that Epicurus or any of his followers held such a doctrine, still it might be asserted with some reason that it is an entirely logical inference from the doctrine of Atomic Declination. Supposing the power of declining to exist in atoms, and that they exert it, if we endeavour by an effort of imagination to conceive the effect, would it not be something like ' Spontaneity ' which might naturally enough manifest itself in the accidental and unforeseen of circumstance and of human affairs ? But even though it were a logical deduction from one principal Epicurean doctrine, this would not be enough to prove it historically correct. It would merely prove Epicurus guilty of inconsistency. I certainly cannot agree with the remark which M. Guyau somewhere makes that ' in Epicureanism there are no inconsistencies, but only a few false deductions.'

11. Seeing that Epicurus believed in so remarkable a power as Atomic Declination, it is only natural that we should ask, ' What comes of this power in the interval between the atoms flying free in the void and these atoms as combined in the soul of man ?   Does it disappear and cease to act in the whole realm of inorganic matter, and come into activity again, only after a vast interval, in the atoms which compose the soul ?' It would be logical to say that it does not, but that it must work on and manifest itself in masses of matter, in bodies of all kinds. At the same time, I believe that Epicurus and Lucretius did not carry out their doctrine to this logical conclusion. The texts referring to Declination (and we have very full and reliable ones in Lucretius and Cicero) declare that Epicurus applied the doctrine solely in two purposes, to allow the origin of the worlds and to explain our Free-will. Whether logically or illogically, Epicurus makes no reference to the action of Declination in bodies

without life ; probably he believed that the combination
of atoms in masses of dead matter must nullify it, the
swerving of one atom counteracting that of another.
Thus I fancy that he conceived the power, if we may so
speak, to ' re-awake ' in the soul-atoms of living creatures.
It is nowhere stated as a part of Epicurean belief that
Declination, by its activity in inorganic matter, produces
those events which we call ' Chance.'   Epicurus would
not have left a doctrine so important to be merely
inferred from another doctrine implying it.   This is not
his manner.

12. How, then, can Epicurus have explained why this
force should practically disappear when the atoms have
combined in inorganic matter ?   He supposes it still to
remain and work within them while confined in the various
forms of matter, but how comes it to exert no farther
influence ?   How does it work to such different effect
in a rock and in a man ?   One reason has been given
above (see § 6) which may partly explain this.   It seems
to me, so far as we can make out, that Epicurus assumed,
whether reasonably or not, that the power of Declination,
while still remaining and working in the atoms, would be
virtually nullified by various counteracting causes—
by the conditions of the world which, when once it is
formed, tend to hold things together[1] (the same forces
which, when atoms have united in the manner necessary
(*concilium*) to form any kind of substance (*res*), compel
them to remain thus united, and keep matter from
dissolving into atoms)—and partly, he would no doubt
have said, by gravity, which would have a resisting

[1] To a certain extent Lucretius conceives the *plagæ extrinsecus undique* (i. 1042) or *ictus externi* (i. 1055) to act in this way.
The atoms not combined in matter form an ever-tossing ocean,
which is constantly beating against the surface of every object.
These continual shocks produce a pressure from without which
tends to hold things together, and to keep the world in existence—

' Summum
Conservare omnem quæcumque est conciliata.'
i. 1042-43.

influence.[1] Besides, Free-will is proportionally a far feebler power in gross matter, formed of coarse atoms (which are also heavier and harder to move), than it is in the soul, which is composed of exceedingly fine and smooth ones. Thus Free-will would exist in far less intensity in gross matter than in the soul, and be far more easily held in check. Such considerations must naturally have kept Epicurus from allowing that masses of matter can decline as the atoms can. For one thing, Lucretius is very conscious (and naturally enough) that an atomic chance-made world, such as he conceives ours to be, is exceedingly liable to destruction, and may any day in a moment fall into ruins and pass away. It is curious how often he reminds us of the many possible causes which might bring this about. Thus, when he is describing the old age of the world (which he always *treats* as if it were an organism), he shows at some length how it must by degrees come to lose more daily than it can assimilate, and how its substance must ebb and waste away, while all the time it is being battered by ' blows ' from without.[2] If Lucretius had believed in Spontaneity as an active force in masses of matter, would he not certainly have been compelled to mention it here as assisting those forces which tend to loose the bonds of the world and break it up ? Would it not have appeared to him that the existence of such a power as ' the declination of heavy bodies ' would render it enormously more difficult for a world, formed like ours, to hold together ?

But still more would Lucretius have conceived such a power as this to interfere with the coming of the world into being. When the atoms, after infinite tossing about from all eternity, ' have at last struck into the proper motions ' to produce the world, these motions are permanent : they last ' through many great years.'

[1] We may contrast the influence assigned to gravity at ii. 288, 289.

[2] II. 1105-74.

> Omne genus motus et cœtus experiundo
> Tandem deveniunt in tales disposituras
> Quibus hæc rerum consistit summa creata
> Et multos etiam magnos servata per annos
> *Ut semel in motus conjectast convenientis.*[1]

It is essential that these motions, attained only as the crown of a long process, after infinite other combinations have been tried and failed, should be preserved unaltered and unmodified. But how is this possible if Spontaneity is to be every moment at work ? In this way the *convenientis motus*, which are vital to the existence of the world, would soon be disturbed and destroyed.[2]

But apart from this, certainly a thinker so shrewd as Epicurus could hardly have conceived such a power to exist in bodies *without also seeing that this would interfere more or less with the regularity of Law in Nature*, a fact which he so firmly and thoroughly grasped.

Students of philosophy have generally taken Guyau's theory for granted on the strength of his brilliant reputation. Thus, Professor Sidgwick (*Mind*, October, 1879) says : ' M. Guyau defends vigorously the well-known *clinamen*. . . . He shows the mistake of supposing that Epicurus attributed this spontaneity to his atoms only in the origination of the world, afterwards suspending its exercise, and he plausibly suggests, on the strength chiefly of a passage of Plutarch[3] (" De Sollertia animal," 7), that

[1] I. 1026-30.

[2] Zeller insists justly on this last point in a brief criticism of Guyau's theory, contained in a note in the latest edition of his ' Stoics, Epicureans, and Sceptics ' (Berlin, 1881, p. 408). He entirely rejects the theory, saying : ' There is no single utterance known to us, either of Epicurus or of one of his followers, which could either express or imply such an assumption ' (In the few lines of his note he does not refer to Lucr., ii. 243-250). He adds : ' If Epicurus held the interference of the Gods in the course of the world to be incompatible with human tranquillity, then he would of necessity have held a continual spontaneous interference of the countless atoms in the course of things to be no less incompatible with it.' (This note is omitted in the English translation of 1901.)

[3] Guyau's partial version and the entire passage from Plutarch are quoted side by side above (at p. 81).

the τύχη which Epicurus admitted as a third cause, side by
side with mechanical necessity and Free-will, was merely
the form in which this essential spontaneity reveals itself
to us.'   So logically consistent with part of Epicurean
doctrine is M. Guyau's theory, so ingeniously and ably
does he defend it, that it is not wonderful that Professor
Sidgwick should have assumed its truth.   The theory is
fascinating in its way.   Only—Epicurus never held it.

It seems as if the doctrines of all later philosophers
were destined to be rediscovered in Aristotle.   Guyau's
theory is an outgrowth from Aristotle's doctrine of
Spontaneity (τὸ αὐτόματον[1]), which he conceives as ' a
variable element inseparably accompanying " Nature,"
modifying, frustrating, distorting her full purposes,' as
seen in deformities, monstrosities, superfluous organs,
and in other ways.[2]   ' Aristotle views Matter as the
cause of every obstruction of the plastic energy of Form.'
The resistance of Matter to Form ' is the cause of all
contingency in Nature,' whether as manifested in the
unessential qualities of a thing which do not appear in
every individual of a class—e.g., blueness in the eyes—or
in those human actions which issue in results not contemplated—e.g., a voyager setting sail for one place,
but carried by a storm to another.[3]   Aristotle defines
' Spontaneity ' as occurring, strictly speaking, only in
things without life, but ' Fortune ' (τύχη) where reasoning
beings are concerned, the results of both being unpre-
dictable.   But surely in any human action where one is
concerned both must be so, more or less.

No thinking mind can stop at ' Fortune ' as a cause
of anything in human experience—e.g., what thought
or feeling prompted the traveller to choose a given vessel
which is destined to be driven from its course, or to sail
on that occasion ?

' It chanced.   Some chance that chance did guide.'

[1] He discusses it specially in his ' Physics,' II., chaps. iv.-vi.
[2] Grote's ' Aristotle,' second edition, p. 115.
[3] See Zeller's ' Aristotle,' English translation, vol. i., p. 359 ff.

Just as little can we stop at Fate as the cause of things. However intricately woven, however far-reaching, link beyond link, be the iron chain-work which, the fatalist tells us, imprisons every human life beyond escape, the possibility of suggestion from without reaching the mind of the human actor severs that chain-work as the shears slits through the most closely-woven web.

Naturally Epicurus was repelled from a system like Aristotle's, which conceived the Divine thought to be everywhere immanent in the world, more or less completely dominating matter, expressing itself in animal, plant, or stone.   But the Aristotelian theory of Spontaneity conflicted with Epicurus's teaching in one way almost as absolutely as did the doctrine of Forms in another.

It is needless to point out the close relation of M. Guyau's doctrine of Spontaneity-in-things to the philosophy of Schopenhauer. Guyau conceives ' Spontaneity ' and Schopenhauer ' Will ' to exist in Matter under its every form, attended by a greater or less degree of consciousness.   The German philosopher sees in Will the real essence of the inorganic world, as well as of vegetable and of animal life.   He applies to the operation of natural forces, such as heat, gravity, electricity, words which, consistently with his doctrine, are specially sought out from the vocabulary describing the efforts of human beings, in whom Will takes its highest form. ' When we attentively consider with what irresistible *striving* water hurls itself into a hollow, the *perseverance* with which the magnet turns to the north, the *ardent desire* of the iron to cling to the magnet, the *violence* with which the two opposite poles of electricity seek to rejoin ; when we observe with what rapidity, with what regularity of shape, with what determined *effort* in fixed directions the crystals form ; when we reflect with what *elective choice* bodies in the fluid state *seek* and *fly* from each other, *unite* and *part ;* when we find, in short, within ourselves a burden, as it were, the *striving* of which towards the terrestrial mass drags down our body, . . . we shall require no great effort of imagination to recognize that that which in us follows a fixed end in the light of intelligence, and that which in the world is but a blind, deaf, limited, invariable tendency, is one and the same thing—almost as the dawn and the full noon are both due to the rays of the sun—and that this thing is will. . . . The objectivation of will, becoming gradually more distinct, manifests itself in the vegetable world. . . . One plant wills a moist situation, another a dry, another a lofty one ; one strives towards the light, the other towards the water. The climbing plant seeks a support ; the tree cracks rocks or bursts a wall by the persistent effort which it makes to develop itself, and so on. All which things are due to the inferior form of will, which Schopenhauer calls excitation.'[1] We quote at such length in order to show how other philosophers besides M. Guyau have found in Nature the manifestations of Will. Not that the two doctrines coincide, for Schopenhauer finds in the inorganic world nothing but cause, working in a fixed order.

M. Guyau has made a vigorous attempt to grasp this cardinal doctrine of Epicurus from every side.[2] Aided by his wide knowledge of both ancient and modern philosophy, he makes us vividly realize the philosophical problem which Epicurus had to encounter, and also his solution of it. Even while disagreeing with him, few will read this very remarkable chapter without feeling that he has flashed light round him. And the picture of Epicurus which his book gives us is drawn not only with great literary skill, but with real philosophic grasp and penetration. Epicureanism, indeed, owes much to French

[1] This abstract, containing almost the words of Schopenhauer, is translated from M. Ribot's ' Philosophie de Schopenhauer ' (Paris, 1874, pp. 76-78).

[2] Notably, however, M. Guyau omits to touch in any way on the subtle adaptation between Atomic Declination and Epicurean psychology—a point which I have attempted to indicate in Volume I., Chapter IX., pp. 207-209.

scholarship, from Gassendi to M. Martha, whose ' Étude sur Lucrèce ' is an admirable study of the ' De Rerum Natura ' in its poetic and moral aspects, and, finally, to M. Guyau.

Although the theory of ' Spontaneity ' so ingeniously set forth by M. Guyau was no part of Epicurean belief, it is still an interesting, and a memorable one.[1] After the notion of Spontaneity working in the material substances everywhere around us, and having power to produce all that in daily life we call Chance or accident, has entered into the mind, it is a thought which, however unreasonable in some respects, one cannot help recurring to. Whatever distant suggestion of truth it may contain, we instinctively reflect that Nature is terrible enough and the world hard enough for man without the interference of a blind, uncontrollable power like this, whose laws we could never hope to master, and which would ever and again transform the regular order of Nature into a mere ' Come what will.'   Still, M. Guyau's theory has even a certain philosophical value, and, whether in its supposed connection with Epicureanism or for its own sake, it will, I believe, from time to time be returned to and discussed afresh.

NOTE ON PROFESSOR G. S. BRETT'S ' PHILOSOPHY OF GASSENDI.'

A book has just been published on ' The Philosophy of Gassendi,' by Professor G. S. Brett, an acute and able work. He comments on the ' Note on Gassendi ' in a former work of mine on ' The Atomic Theory of Lucretius,' and is not aware that the whole passage has been

[1] Does not the notion of ' Spontaneity ' in things remind us a little—of course, merely in certain aspects—of Goethe's ' Dæmonic Principle '?   In Goethe's own words, ' the Dæmonic is that which cannot be explained by reason and understanding.'   It ' resembles Chance, for it evolves no consequences.'   It manifests itself not in man merely, but ' in all corporeal and incorporeal things.'   ' It is particularly perceptible in events, and, indeed, in all which we cannot explain by reason and understanding.'

rewritten and greatly enlarged in the present work (see Volume I., pp. 237-241), a fact which renders his criticisms largely superfluous.

The following is probably, *on the whole*, correct, though it seems to contradict Gassendi's own expressions in many places :

' Gassendi would not entertain the idea of potential presence, and therefore the statement that the particles do not possess consciousness " actually " means that they do not possess it at all. As I have tried to show, Gassendi, for better or for worse, prefers to take it that the peculiar properties of each degree of organic life cannot be found in the parts as they are before they are found in the synthesis of the organism, but supervene on the fact of that synthesis. The effects are data to be co-ordinated, not explained. Gassendi would have said of Nature, as a whole, what James says of mental phenomena—that the square of a plus that of b is not the same as the square of $(a+b)$ ' (p. 118).

Of course, this illustration from algebra goes only a certain way. Not everything can be ' squared ' as numerals can. Elsewhere he says :

' I conclude that Gassendi's real view of the soul makes it one in all entities, from the stones to man, but with such obvious distinctions of degree that it is no loss practically to admit differences of kind : the common denominator cannot be shown ' (p. 114).

Some term must be found according to which the degrees of life can be formulated, and Gassendi employs the term of ' motion ' as the common denominator. Thus, as to the magnet, ' Gassendi is not trying to prove that the magnet has a kind of feeling, as we know it in consciousness, but that the common denominator of the whole scale is motile response ' (p. 119).

On the subject of Atomic Declination, Professor Brett has propounded a solution which imposes on Lucretius and Epicurus notions which are entirely foreign to both

of them.   Criticizing some words of mine, he says : ' The
fatis avolsa potestas of Lucretius seems to have made
Masson think that Lucretius exempted the Will from
determination, though *surely Lucretius must have seen
that one lawless element makes the whole lawless.*   Masson's
assumption seems to be that Law holds in Nature only :
hence Guyau's spontaneity in Nature must be a fiction.
But *the animus which we labour to make free is also in
Nature*, and therefore its spontaneity is a fiction.'

The passages which I have italicized involve a curious
misunderstanding of Lucretius's position, which is that
the human will is free in a universe otherwise determined
by unbending laws.   On no other basis can his argument
for Free-will be understood, as I have pointed out in
Appendices VII. and XVI. (see also p. 75, notes 1 and 2,
of the present chapter).

Mr. Brett continues :

' Lucretius exactly formulates the position in the phrase
" *fatisque avolsa potestas* " (Book II., l. 257).   The apparent
meaning of that is " a power plucked from the grip of
Fate "—*i.e.*, saved from the inexorable laws.   But that
is just what it does not mean ; on the contrary, it means
" saved from the Fates in order to be subject to law."
The Fates denote here the power which overrules physical
laws. . . .   *Fate, then, is the contrary of regular law-abiding
action.*   Hence Gassendi says : " Explodenda Democriti
sententia est . . . illa Epicuri defendi quidem potest
quatenus Fatum et Naturam naturaleisve causas res
esse synonymas ducit."   It was, then, by making Fate
the same as Nature that Epicurus defended freedom !
This seems paradoxical, but the difference lies just in
this — that Democritus said Nature is Fate, and in any
case we are bound hand and foot ; Epicurus said Fate
is nothing unless it is law, *and the law is my nature*, not
something *extrinsecus* overruling me.   So long, says
Epicurus, as natural forces alone control action, I am
free, for I am a real agent,' etc. (p. 238).

What authority has Mr. Brett for putting in Epicurus's

mouth the notion that ' The law is my nature ' ?   ' Fate '
and ' Nature ' are synonymous for Lucretius in reference
to the outer world only.   We have not here to reason out
the problem as a modern metaphysician might do, but
to ascertain Epicurus's actual opinion, whether Mr.
Brett may think it consistent or not.   Nor can I believe,
from a careful study of the passage and its context, that
Gassendi represents Epicurus to mean this.

At p. 225 Professor Brett says that Gassendi holds
the atoms to have been created with given properties
and ' determinations,' and adds : ' In this point Gassendi
is really enlarging the hint given by Lucretius, who had
introduced the idea of atoms as *semina rerum*, which
implies that certain lines of development were prescribed.'
Any such distinction is foreign to Lucretius.   To him the
term *semina rerum* is merely a synonym for atoms, which
means that these possess, quite fortuitously, the faculty
of entering into combinations and producing things.

Gassendi himself uses *semina rerum* to mean ' molecules ' (of course, not in the strict sense of modern chemistry), not ' atoms.'   He defines it thus :

' Ex atomis conformari primum moleculas quasdam
inter se diversas quae sint semina rerum : ac deinde res
quasque ex seminibus suis ita texi atque constitui ut
neque sint neque esse possint ex aliis ' [*Animadversiones*, I.,
p. 108].

PART II
APPENDICES

APPENDIX I

ORIGIN OF LEUCIPPUS'S ATOMIC THEORY

It is to be noted that, as Windelband says, ' The Atomic theory which became later so important in science did not grow out of experiment or observation, and the conclusions built upon them, but directly out of the abstractest metaphysical concepts.'

Leucippus stood in the closest relation to the Eleatic school. His Atomism is to be regarded as a variant of the Eleatic metaphysics, which asserted that all Being is One, because all that exists is in its essence the same. Like the Eleatics, he denied the reality of Becoming, and held that ' Being ' excluded not only origination and destruction, but also all change. Along with the Eleatics, he regarded ' Being ' as coinciding with extended matter. Parmenides had felt that this coincidence compelled him to deny the reality of empty space, and therefore also of plurality of things and of motion. If, as he held, the Universe is one continuous, extended mass, nowhere broken by Non-Being, there is no place for anything to move into ; motion, therefore, is an illusion. But here Leucippus took his own road. He asserted that ' Being ' is no more real than ' Non-Being,' that Void space does actually exist, that ' Something ' is no wise more real than ' Nothing.' This is the main principle of the atomistic metaphysics. Thus, as observation of the actual world began to demand, plurality and motion became possible.

But, while he deserted Parmenides here, Leucippus held

fast to his doctrine of the unchangeableness and absolute homogeneity of ' Being.' He agreed with Parmenides that this homogeneity consists in abstract corporeality (τὸ πλέον), devoid of all specific qualities, but possessing extension in space.   But the matter filling space and the void itself cannot merely exist side by side if we are to explain the world from them.   The plurality of things in the world, the distinctions of form and motion that observation shows us, are due to the penetration of ' Being ' by ' Non-Being,' of Matter by Void.   The Plenum must be divided by the Vacuum.   (This division cannot go on to infinity, breaking matter down to nothing at all ; for, according to Leucippus and the Eleatics, ' Being ' is defined as indivisible Unity.   The atoms may be infinite in number, but, as homogeneous, they are Unity.)   Each of the substances possessing ' Being ' must, then, be thought of as corporeal, homogeneous, absolutely solid, and therefore indivisible.   ' Being,' therefore, consists of innumerable exceedingly small bodies.   Leucippus called these ' Atoms ' (ἄτομοι).   Every one of these is like the single cosmic Being of Parmenides—unoriginated, unchangeable, indivisible.   Were not these particles separated by empty space, they would constitute but a single ' element,' in the sense of Empedocles, and would, indeed, be the absolute qualitativeless ' Being ' of the Eleatics.

In this account I have chiefly followed Windelband, who treats the subject very ably (' Geschichte der Alten Philosophie,' English Translation, 1900).

According to Windelband, Leucippus did not seek the cause of motion in a force different from matter.   He regards motion as immanent in matter.   The corporeality which in all atoms is homogeneous possesses, in virtue of its own essence, an original underived motion.[1]   This motion is not gravity, a fall from above downward, but a chaotic disorderly movement of the atoms in all directions.

[1] Windelband here presses far too strongly the phrase ἀπὸ ταὐτομάτου (Aristotle, ' Phys.,' ii. 4).

This last is the view of Brieger (' Die Urbewegung der Atome bei Leucipp und Democrit,' 1884). Zeller, in his fifth edition (Leipzig, 1897, pp. 874-888), defends with great force and ability the older view. He contends that, as both Leucippus and Democritus held, as nothing happens in the world without natural causes, even what is apparently fortuitous, the motion of the atoms is no exception : its cause is gravitation ;[1] they attributed to atoms weight proportional to their size. Unlike Epicurus, they assumed the rate of the fall of the atoms to differ according to their weight, and collisions to arise in consequence.

With regard to this controversy, two things are clear : Firstly, the difficulty that in infinite space there is no Above and no Down did not trouble the early Atomists ; secondly, as Aristotle implies, they did not express themselves with distinctness as to the original motion of tl e atoms.

[1] Is it correct to say with Windelband (§ 32) that ' weight ' in early Atomism very often means merely ' movableness,' while in Epicureanism it includes ' fall ' ?

APPENDIX II

BESIDES two collections of sayings, three epistles have
been preserved by Diogenes Laërtius bearing the name of
Epicurus. Usener considers the first of these, ' To Hero-
dotus,' as of unquestionable authority ; the second, ' To
Pythocles,' he considers to be compiled possibly by
Epicurus himself from his great work in thirty-seven
books, ' On Nature '; and the third, ' To Menœceus,' as
Epicurus's own composition; this last showing, as do
some of the sayings, that on occasion he could write
both with point and elegance.[1]

The first of these is referred to in the letter to Pythocles
as the ' Small Abridgment ' (μικρὰ ἐπιτομή). Lucretius
appears not to have followed to any extent the method of
treatment found in this letter, which not improbably was
a summary of the 'Great Abridgment' (μεγάλη ἐπιτομή),
repeatedly referred to by Diogenes (x. 39, 40, 73). Both
Brieger and Giussani regard the latter work as that which
Lucretius mainly followed. They do not, however, give
any adequate reason for fixing on this work as specially
' the source of the poem.' We can only guess at the
relation between the contents of the ' small ' and the
' great ' abridgment. Whether, for instance, the twenty-
eight proofs of the mortality of the soul laid down by
Lucretius were given in the latter we cannot tell. It is
most unlikely that so devoted a disciple as Lucretius
should not have made constant use of Epicurus's great
work, ' On Nature.'

[1] ' Epicurea,' pp. xxxvii. ff.

Giussani, in his section on the authorities used by Lucretius,[1] deals chiefly with the first letter, as to which he and Usener differ widely. Usener has proved beyond question that Diogenes gave the three epistles (without having read them through or scarce even inspected them) to a scribe to be copied. The scribe copied them in full, not forgetting the scholia in the margin, which he inserted in the text in the most thoughtless fashion, sometimes in the middle of a sentence, so as to confuse the sense. These scholia are evidently the work of a man well read in Epicurus's works.[2] Giussani maintains at great length that the confused sequence of the first letter is due to the ignorance and carelessness of the copyist. (Yet he admits that the writer of these scholia had the letter before him in its present form.) Brieger convincingly proves that the existing order (or disorder) of the sections is the original form of the treatise ; and this, he believes, comes from Epicurus himself.[3] It is, therefore, idle to attempt, as Giussani does, to rearrange its parts. We have here a compendium, formed of sentences to be learned by heart, and these may partly have been copied by Epicurus out of his ' Large Abridgment,' partly set down from memory with variations, not concerning himself as to their logical order or connection. Thus, this epistle is lacking in the perspicuity and plainness which Cicero attributes to Epicurus's regular treatises.[4] But this does not justify an attempt to rearrange the letter in an order adapted to modern notions.

As to Lucretius's criticisms of other philosophers, his

[1] ' Osservazioni intorno a qualche fonte di Lucrezio,' *Studi*, pp. 1-20.

[2] ' Epicurea,' p. xxvii.

[3] *Jahresberichte*, 1896, pp. 181-185. See also his pamphlet, ' Epikur's Brief an Herodot,' 1882, an acute examination of the structure of the letter.

[4] After explaining that he can pardon Epicurus for lacking the ' ornamenta orationis ' of Plato and others, he adds : ' Oratio me istius philosophi non offendit : nam et complectitur verbis quod vult et dicit plane quod intelligam ' (' De Fin.,' i., c. 5).

knowledge may have been obtained directly from their writings, or more probably, Brieger thinks, from a controversial treatise by ' some later Epicurean, superior to his master in literary and philosophic culture.' This Giussani will not allow. Brieger concludes with the remark : ' I here emphatically repeat that Giussani overestimates Epicurus as thinker and man of learning in a fashion which is dangerous, positively dangerous, for the understanding of the coarsely rough-hewn doctrines of his master.'

I find it hard to believe, from the tone in which Lucretius speaks of each, that he did not know Democritus, and especially Empedocles, at first hand. Another poet who influenced him deeply was Euripides, whose ' Iphigenia in Aulis ' he has repeatedly imitated, in one case translating a line.[1] Euripides's criticism of Greek religion, especially in those five plays which deal with the subject of human sacrifice in order to appease offended Gods, must have profoundly appealed to the young poet.

[1] Compare Lucr., i. 44—

    ' Quod patrio princeps donarat nomine regem '—
with ' Iph. in A.,' 1222—

$$\pi\rho\acute{\omega}\tau\eta\ \sigma'\ \acute{\epsilon}\kappa\acute{\alpha}\lambda\epsilon\sigma\alpha\ \pi\alpha\tau\acute{\epsilon}\rho\alpha\ \kappa\alpha\grave{\iota}\ \sigma\grave{\upsilon}\ \pi\alpha\grave{\iota}\delta'\ \acute{\epsilon}\mu\acute{\epsilon}.$$

APPENDIX III

IN a pamphlet[1] entitled 'Science, Prayer, Free-will, and
Miracles' (Burns and Oates, 1881), an able Roman
Catholic writer (Dr. W. G. Ward) effectively criticized
the reasoning of Tyndall and others. Dr. Ward's conception of a 'Divine premovement' of events is by no
means a novel one, though it has never before been
worked out with so much force and grasp. He has re-
course to a somewhat grotesque illustration, which, however, helps us to realize the question vividly enough. He
imagines some mice, endowed with human or quasi-
human intelligence, to be shut up in a musical instrument
like a piano, but 'immeasurably more vast in size and
more complex in machinery.' In this instrument the
intermediate links between the player's premovement
on the one hand, and the resulting sound on the other,
are not two only, as in a piano, but two hundred. On the
polychordon someone is unintermittently playing, but
playing on it just what airs may strike his fancy at the
moment. The mice hear the music, and philosophize as
to its origin. Successive generations of philosophical
mice have actually traced one hundred and fifty of the
two hundred phenomenal sequences through whose fixed
and invariable laws the sound is produced. The colony
of mice, shut up within, are delighted with the success
which has crowned the labours of their leading thinkers,

---

[1] Reprinted in 'Essays on the Philosophy of Theism,' 2 vols.,
1884.

and the most eminent of these addresses an assembly as follows : ' We have long known that the laws of our musical universe are immutably fixed ; but we have now discovered a far larger number of those laws than our ancestors could have imagined *capable* of discovery. Let us redouble our efforts. I fully expect that our grand-children will be able to predict as accurately, for an indefinitely preceding period, the succession of melodies with which we are to be delighted, as we now predict the hours of sunrise and sunset. One thing, at all events, is now absolutely incontrovertible. As to the notion of there being some agency *external* to the polychordon—intervening with arbitrary and capricious will to produce the sounds we experience—this is a long-exploded superstition, a mere dream and dotage of the past. The progress of science has put it on one side, and never again can it return to disturb our philosophical progress.' The meaning of Dr. Ward's parable is clear. Two hundred absolutely fixed laws intervene between the player's pre-movement and the resulting sound ; but this fact does not tend ever so remotely to show that there is not an intelligent player, or that his premovement is not absolutely unremitting. In like manner, though scientific men have discovered that the laws of Nature are absolutely fixed, and though we have already mastered many of them, this ' *would not tend ever so remotely to show that those laws are not at each moment directed to this purpose or to that by an immediate and uncontrolled Divine Premovement.* God's real ends cannot be more inscrutable to us . . . than would be the ends of a human performer to the mice within this supposed polychordon. . . . And as a player on the polychordon may readily be induced, at the smallest request of a little child, to produce this particular musical result rather than some other, so the heartfelt prayer of the humblest Christian may powerfully affect God's pre-movement of the physical world.'[1] Dr. Ward's illustra-

---

[1] ' Think of the swiftness of lightning. Yet how vastly finer are the atoms of the soul ! In prayer actual atoms go out from

tion of the philosophical mice brings the question home,
and makes it palpable in a way that excuses its grotesque-
ness.—He further draws a distinction, important for this
subject, between *cosmical* phenomena, such as the hours
of sunrise and sunset, or the periodical return of comets
and eclipses, which are produced by an incredibly vast
machinery, in which this earth plays a very subordinate
part, and earthly phenomena, such as the weather, the
violence of the wind, and disease, which are due in great
measure to agencies acting exclusively within the region
of our planet. The course of cosmical phenomena is
steady, and amenable to calculation, while the course of
earthly phenomena is variable and incalculable. Prayer
has to do with the latter exclusively. ' It is most remarkable, and bears thinking of again and again, that the only
power of indefinite prediction which science has ever procured, concerns cosmical phenomena, and not earthly.'
Again, if God premoves earthly phenomena, why does He
will that their causation should be so complex ? Dr.
Ward replies most forcibly : ' It is not the general law of
God's Providence that the truths of religion *shall* be
visible and palpable facts ; but, on the contrary, that
they shall give occasion to the merit of faith. Let it be
assumed, then, that God does premove earthly phenomena, and let the further very obvious supposition be
also made that He does not desire this premovement to
be a visible and palpable fact. On this supposition, He
would act just as we maintain that He has acted. *He
would make earthly phenomena to proceed on so complex a
chain of causation that His assiduous premovement of them
eludes direct observation.*'

Dr. Ward's theory of a Divine premovement is admirably stated, but have not all really spiritual natures

---

the soul in its supreme effort to God. Have the other gross
elemental forces in Nature power ? and shall so fine an element
with so fine atoms have no power ?' (from a sermon by John
Pulsford). The smallness of a force is nothing if it can make
itself felt at the very springs of action.

worked out the problem much in this way—namely, that God is *always* at work, *everywhere* in Nature ? To certain minds the existence of fixed laws which produce results, seemingly of themselves, forms an insurmountable barrier to the recognition of God. Yet even though He work beyond so vast and intricate a wheelwork of natural laws, men like Socrates have not failed to realize, with more or less completeness, the Divine hand behind all the intermediate machinery.

The theory of the sub-conscious self so admirably set forth by Professor William James (' Varieties of Religious Experience,' 1902) carries an infinite suggestiveness for the whole problem of Premovement in the sphere of mind.

The problem is most ably handled by Sir Oliver Lodge in his latest book (' Man and the Universe,' 1908). He says :

' The root question or outstanding controversy between science and faith rests upon two distinct conceptions of the universe : the one, that of a self-contained and self-sufficient universe, with no outlook into or links with anything beyond, uninfluenced by any life or mind except such as is connected with a visible and tangible material body ; and the other conception, that of a universe lying open to all manner of spiritual influences, permeated through and through with a Divine spirit, guided and watched by living minds, acting through the medium of law indeed, but with intelligence and love behind the law—a universe by no means self-sufficient or self-contained, but with sensitive tendrils groping into another supersensuous order of existence.'

In the first case, of course, prayer is absurd and childish.

That the All is a manifestation of God may be readily granted. It would be strange to include only mountains and trees, and the visible material universe, and exclude the intelligence, and will, and emotion, and personality of which we ourselves are conscious. Any power, any love of our own must exist in intensified form in the totality of things, or else we make the grotesque assumption that in all the infinite universe we men are the highest.

Are we to believe in irrefragable law or in spiritual guidance? The two beliefs, Sir Oliver insists, are not inconsistent with each other.

He lays down two propositions :

' 1. We must realize that the Whole is a single un-deviating, law-saturated cosmos ;

' 2. But we must also realize that the Whole consists not of matter and motion alone, nor yet of spirit and will alone, but of both and all.'

Scientific men have been liable to take a narrow view of the second of these principles, while religious men have been tempted to substitute a world of caprice for a strictly orderly cosmos. To those who are able to combine both beliefs, prayer is quite consistent with an orderly universe, ' for it may represent a portion of the guiding and controlling Will.'

The question how Mind can act on Matter now confronts us. Vitality is clearly the intermediary. Sir Oliver returns here to the contention of his former work (' Life and Mind,' 1905) that life is not a force nor an energy, but only a guiding and directing influence. ' It affects the quantity of energy no whit,' ' I mean by " guiding " the influencing of activity without " work," the directing of energy without generating it, the utiliza-tion of pre-existent activity for preconceived and purposed ends.' Even in mechanics we see this. A railway guides a train to its destination, the engine supplies the energy ; life and mind have determined where the rails shall be laid, when and whence and whither the trains are to be run, but they exert no iota of force upon these.

Life and mind on the one side ; body and mechanism on the other belong to separate categories. The brain is the mysterious connector between the physical and psychical worlds which otherwise could not be in touch. The mind ' apparently has the power of liberating detents or pulling hair-triggers ' in that strange connector. How it can do this is not known ('Man and the Universe,' section I, pp. 1-80).

If 'life' includes will, should not Sir Oliver Lodge's statement that it 'affects the quantity of energy no whit' be modified or qualified ?   Before the Will can 'liberate a detent or pull a hair-trigger' in the brain-cell, must it not have the power, if not of originating, yet of transferring or transmitting *some* energy, *however small ?* No more than is required to move a single molecule from its place for an inconceivably minute distance might suffice, as Sir John Herschell suggests (see the passage quoted in explaining the subtle part played by Declination in 'Epicurean Psychology,' vol. i., p. 208). We are vividly, directly conscious that *somehow* our will has the power to exert force upon matter.

APPENDIX IV

DIFFERENT SHAPES OF THE ATOMS

In the following passage Theophrastus, a contemporary of Epicurus, describes the different forms of the atoms. He refers to the atomic theory of Democritus :

Δημόκριτος δὲ σχῆμα περιτιθεὶς ἑκάστῳ, γλυκὺν μὲν τὸν στρογγύλον καὶ εὐμεγέθη ποιεῖ· στρυφνὸν δὲ τὸν μεγαλόσχημον, τραχὺν[1] τε καὶ πολυγώνιον καὶ ἀπεριφερῆ· ὀξὺν δὲ κατὰ τοὔνομα τὸν ὀξὺν τῷ ὄγκῳ καὶ κωνοειδῆ (γωνιοειδῆ Schneider) καὶ καμπύλον καὶ λεπτὸν καὶ ἀπεριφερῆ· δριμὺν δὲ τὸν περιφερῆ καὶ λεπτὸν καὶ γωνιοειδῆ καὶ καμπύλον· ἁλμυρὸν δὲ τὸν γωνιοειδῆ καὶ εὐμεγέθη (?) καὶ σκολιὸν καὶ ἰσοσκελῆ· πικρὸν δὲ τὸν περιφερῆ καὶ λεῖον, ἔχοντα σκολιότητα μέγεθος δὲ μικρόν· λιπαρὸν δὲ τὸν λεπτὸν καὶ στρογγύλον καὶ μικρόν[2] ('De Causis Plantarum,' vi. 1, ed. Schneider, 1818).

In another treatise Theophrastus again expounds at great length Democritus's explanation of differences of taste, as caused by atoms of different shape touching the tongue. We quote the following :

τὸν δὲ πικρὸν ἐκ μικρῶν καὶ λείων καὶ περιφερῶν, ἀλλ' ἐπ'

---

[1] Gassendi, as quoted below, evidently read τραχὺν δὲ τὸν πολυγώνιον.

[2] Gassendi translates thus :

'Rotundas videlicet esse congruaque mole, quæ Dulcem faciant ; magna figura, quæ Acerbum ; multangula minimeque orbiculari, quæ Asperum ; acuta, conica, incurva, non tenui, non rotunda quæ Acutum ; orbiculata, tenui, angulata, incurva quæ Acrem ; angulata, distorta, crurumque æqualium, quæ Salsum ; rotunda, levi, distorta, parva quæ Amarum ; tenui, rotunda, parka quæ Pinguem' ('Animadversiones,' 1675, vol. i., p. 156).

111

ἐνίων μὲν σκαληνῶν, διὸ οὐδὲ πολυκάμπτων· βούλεται δὲ σκαληνὰ λέγειν, ἅπερ παράλλαξιν[1] ἔχει πρὸς ἄλληλα καὶ συμπλοκὴν ('De Sensu et Sensilibus,' c. lxvi.). See other passages from Theophrastus collected and translated in Mullach's separate edition of Democritus (Berlin, 1843, pp. 217 ff.). Scholars now hold that the 'Placita Philosophorum' of the Pseudo-Plutarch are derived from Theophrastus's great work, περὶ φυσικῶν δοξῶν.

Cicero thus refers to the atoms of Democritus:

'Asperis et levibus et hamatis uncinatisque corporibus concreta hæc esse' ('Acad.,' ii. 121). 'Esse corpuscula, quædam levia, alia aspera, rotunda alia, partim angulata et pyramidata, curvata quædam et quasi adunca' ('De Natura Deorum,' i. 66).

We may compare Gassendi:

'Non posse quidem mentem assequi illam tantam varietatem figurarum, quæ adscribendæ sunt atomis; cum sint rotundæ, ovatæ, lenticulares, planæ, gibbæ, oblongæ, turbinatæ, hamatæ, læves, asperæ, hispidæ, tetrahedricæ, pentahedricæ, hexahedricæ, etc., tam regulares quam irregulares, absque determinatione ulla intellectui possibili, ac potissimum irregularitatis formas commiscendo' (vol. i., p. 113).

Gassendi refutes the objection that atoms with slender projecting points must be liable to fracture, by saying that, since every part of the atom is perfectly solid and contains no void, atoms furnished with angles or apices or hooks are as indestructible as spherical atoms are.[2]

---

[1] Does παράλλαξιν πρὸς ἄλληλα mean 'overlapping each other'?

[2] 'Perspicuum est Atomos, qualescumque sint, corpuscula esse solidissima, inanisque plane expertia, quare et cum hami angulique ejusdem sint soliditatis, . . . necesse est ipsos tam resistere ictibus externis, quam ipsa corpuscula orbicularia' (ibid., vol. i., p. 115).

APPENDIX V

OUR notion of the atom has been so altered by the great
discovery of Radio-Activity that some account of this
must be given. In 1896 Becquerel discovered that both
uranium and its salts, even although they had not been
exposed to sunlight, emitted a radiation which resembled
the X rays in its power of penetrating opaque bodies and
affecting the photographic plate. In 1898 the Curies
discovered radium in pitchblende, from which it is extracted in the proportion of $\frac{3}{20}$ of a gramme to a ton of
the material. The ray-emitting power of radium is
enormous. The metal has never yet been isolated, and is
employed for experimental purposes chiefly in the form
of chloride or bromide. With two exceptions—viz.,
thorium (atomic weight, 232·5) and uranium (atomic
weight, 238·5), both of which are also radio-active,
although in a much slighter degree—it has the highest
weight of all the known elements—namely, 225.[1] It
gives off three kinds of rays : a-rays, consisting of streams
of positively electrified atoms ; β-rays, formed of negative
ions or ' corpuscles,' which are commonly called ' electrons,' much smaller than atoms, say $\frac{1}{1000}$ part the mass
of hydrogen atoms ; and γ-rays, which appear to be
X rays or some type of these. The velocity of these
rays is inconceivably great ; they fly enormously faster
than the swiftest bullet or cannon-ball. But the three-

[1] According to Thorpe (May, 1908), it is 227.

fold rays do not explain the whole mystery of radium. It also gives off something distinct and apart from the rays themselves which is called ' an emanation,' and which causes the bodies in the neighbourhood of radium to acquire an induced radio-activity. This emanation is a gas. When a radium salt is heated or dissolved in water, the emanation from it is immensely greater than that discharged from radium in a solid, cold state. This fact appears to concord with the notion that the emanation is a gas of some kind occluded by the radium. The amount of energy radiated by the emanation is incredibly large in proportion to the amount of matter emitting it. The radiation consists entirely of a-rays ; and the emanation retains its power of emitting these rays for some time, while the radium from which the emanation is abstracted loses 75 per cent. of its activity. But in the course of a month the radium recovers all that it has lost, while the emanation loses its radio-activity at the same rate.

' If, as is apparently the case, the radium is constantly generating and storing the emanation and the emanation as constantly decaying, the activity of the radium at any one time is due to a balance between the decaying and restoring processes ; and since, moreover, these processes are wholly outside the sphere of known controllable forces and cannot be created, altered, or destroyed— since the process is independent of the chemical form of the radium, whether bromide, chloride, sulphate, etc.— we are absolutely shut up to the conviction that it is a function of its atom. We are in the presence of a veritable decay of the atom.'[1]

Radio-activity is independent of temperature. If the air containing the emanation is passed over red-hot platinum, zinc, etc., these powerful reagents do not alter its ray-emitting power at all. This fact confirms the view

[1] ' The New Knowledge,' by Professor R. K. Duncan, 1905, pp. 119, 120, to which book I am largely indebted for facts hitherto given. It is an admirably clear account of the discoveries leading up to and resulting from that of radium.

that the energy involved in radio-activity is due to changes going on within the atoms themselves ; for if they were caused by actions between the molecules, it would pretty certainly be affected by temperature.

In March, 1903, Curie and Laborde announced that radium has the power to emit heat without combustion or change in its molecular structure—a fact as remarkable as that a stove should continue red-hot without fuel. Apparently this heat is largely due to the constant bombarding of its mass by the a-particles projected from itself. The heat evolved by the radium emanation is over 3,500,000 times greater than that let loose by any known chemical reaction, such as that of exploding the same volume of hydrogen and oxygen. It cannot, therefore, be due to any ordinary chemical action. This radio-activity, therefore, can only come from a store of energy within the atom. This energy is due to the breaking up of the atom, not of all the atoms of a mass at the same time, probably only of an infinitesimal portion of them. Thus an enormous reservoir of energy is locked up in the atom which science may some day be able to make available.[1]

What a change do these discoveries bring about in our notion of the atom ! It is stripped of its attribute of indivisibility. But it still holds its ground—' It is the fact of definite combining properties among the atoms which makes modern chemistry hold together as a science.'[2]

Whatever may be the case with the chemist, physicists of late tend very largely to regard all the elements as different groupings of one fundamental constituent, which is ' nothing more nor less than electricity in the form of an aggregate of an equal number of positive and negative unit electric charges.'[3] Thus Sir Oliver Lodge suggests we may fancy an atom of hydrogen to consist of, say,

[1] ' The New Knowledge,' pp. 112-121.
[2] Dr. W. W. Ireland, *Journal of Mental Science*, January, 1908.
[3] ' Modern Views on Matter ' (the Romanes Lecture), by Sir Oliver Lodge ; new edition, 1907, p. 13.

700 electrons, 350 positive and 350 negative. On this hypothesis sixteen times as many would constitute an atom of oxygen, while some 16,000 electrons would form an atom of sodium, and 160,000 an atom of radium. According to the same man of science, the mass of the electron is 'of the order $\frac{1}{1000}$ of the atomic mass of hydrogen,' and 'if they are purely and solely electrical their size must be $\frac{1}{100000}$ of the linear dimensions of an atom.' Assuming the thesis which dates virtually from Faraday's time, that every atom of matter can have a certain definite quantity of electricity associated with it, 'if an electron is represented by a sphere an inch in diameter, the diameter of an atom of matter on the same scale is a mile and a half. . . . An atom is not a large thing, but if it is composed of electrons, the spaces between them are enormous compared with their size— as great relatively as are the spaces between the planets in the solar system.'

The atom thus would be an open structure in which the vacant spaces are enormous compared with the tiny corpuscles scattered through them. Thus, if we imagine an atom of hydrogen to be the size of an ordinary church, the corpuscles that constitute the atom would be represented by some 750 grains of sand, each the size of a printer's full stop, dashing in all directions, rotating with inconceivable speed, 'occupying the otherwise empty region of space which we call the atom' much as a few armed soldiers can occupy a territory, 'by forceful activity, not by bodily bulk.'[1]

The discovery of radium and of its properties does not quite take us by surprise. Some dozen years ago it was pointed out that if an atom be a mere system of electrons in violent motion, some day we should find such an atom in the course of breaking up. Radium, having one of the highest atomic weights among the elements, its atom must be formed of the most intricate arrangement of electrons, some 160,000. It is precisely in such an ex-

[1] 'Modern Views on Matter,' pp. 8-13.

tremely complex-structured atom as this that it was mathematically predicted that disintegration would occur. This prediction is now verified. We do not know how to break up these atoms ; from time to time they are liable to explode or break up of themselves.

It must be patent to all from the account above that theory has as yet far outstripped experiment in regard to radio-activity.   The subject is still in such a state of flux that it is hard to say what the prevailing opinions are. In 1904 Professor J. J. Thomson, one of the originators of the electron theory, assumed the ordinary atom to consist of a large number of negative electrons, arranged in concentric circles, in a sphere of uniform positive electrification, in such number that there would be about 1,000 electrons in the hydrogen atom, 16,000 in the oxygen atom, and so on. He showed that such an electrical structure would possess many of the known qualities of atoms.[1] But in 1906, after having examined this hypothesis by three different experimental methods, he came to the conclusion that the number of electrons in the atom is probably of the same order as the atomic weight[2]— that is to say, he reduced his estimate of the number of electrons to $\frac{1}{1000}$ of the former amount ! Not that this is any reproach to the investigator, for science is only now feeling its way in this wide new field. In 1906 Mr. Soddy writes : ' It may be stated without fear of contradiction that the theory that the atom is made up entirely or to any substantial extent of electrons is now generally regarded as being very much open to question. From spectroscopic and other evidence it is certain that electrons are universal constituents of the atoms, but for the further sweeping deduction that the atoms are composed of electrons there has never been much positive evidence

[1] See the chapter on ' The Constitution of the Atom ' in J. J. Thomson's ' Electricity and Matter,' 1904.

[2] See Report on Radio-activity for 1906, p. 351, by Mr. Frederick Soddy, joint-discoverer along with Ramsay of the production of helium from radium ('Annual Reports on the Progress of Chemistry,' published by the Chemical Society).

in the past ; while Professor J. J. Thomson, to whom the electronic theory is largely due, has this year brought forward considerations which have practically made the theory untenable. . . . The result that all but about $\frac{1}{1000}$ of the mass is associated with the positive part of the atom shows that an altogether exaggerated rôle has been attached to the electron in the constitution of matter.'[1] These later investigations of Thomson's, as Mr. Soddy says, ' practically leave the whole problem of the ultimate constitution of matter where it was.'

Again, in 1907, Sir W. Ramsay and Mr. A. T. Cameron, as the result of later experiments, ' suggest that helium and the *a*-particles are not identical, but that helium results as the product by the degradation of the large molecules of emanation under bombardment by the *a*-particles.'[2]

Where there is such divergence among the highest authorities, I cannot imitate the confidence with which one or two critics (none of whom, it is evident, are chemists) have spoken of the electron theory. The data above given form a strange comment upon the complaint of one reviewer of ability that I have not given ' an authoritative exposition of the present position of the atomic theory,' including the theory of electrons.

The electronic theory of the constitution of matter, *if* it can be established, will be ' a unification of matter such as has throughout all the ages been sought—going further, indeed, than had been hoped, for the substratum is not something unknown and hypothetical, but the familiar electric charge.' But from what has been said above it will be obvious that this is a very large ' if '!

A writer in *Nature* (May 28, 1908), on ' The Science of the Electron,' points out that the new electrical theory is very largely Franklin's view of the electrical fluid, elaborated and refurbished. Why, then, is Franklin so

[1] ' Reports ' for 1906, pp. 350, 351.
[2] ' Reports ' for 1907, p. 335.

seldom named in connection with the electron theory ?[1]
The explanation is that the elaboration peculiar to the
modern theory is relatively so important that the mere
assumption of a fluid at all, once taken for granted, is
not worth mentioning.   The main elaboration consists
in assuming that *electricity, like matter, is made up of
discrete portions*, and in speaking of ' molecules of electricity,' as Maxwell did (though he regarded the expression as ' gross ' and ' provisional '), or, otherwise, in
speaking of electrons.'   This conception, however, is so
needful to explain the phenomena connected with the
discharge through gases and radio-activity that it is
rightly introduced as a hypothesis, and has proved fruitful.
But the writer doubts ' if there was ever a time in the
history of physical science when so much unproved hypothesis was employed.'   It has gone quite beyond justifi-
able bounds, as in the notion which explains all inertia
in the same way as the inertia of the electron, the concrete
form of this notion being the supposition that all atoms
are built up of electrons.   This conception the writer
proceeds to criticize.

Speaking of the theoretical interpretation of the new
facts connected with radio-activity in physics, chemistry,
and astronomy, Professor Duncan modestly says : ' This
system of the new knowledge is simply . . . the truest
exposition of the truth attainable at the time, and as such
is vastly useful.   Its utility in the evolution of knowledge
is its sole apology for existence.'[2]

[1] See J. J. Thomson's reference to Franklin in his chapter
on ' The Atomic Structure of Electricity ' (p. 88).
[2] ' The New Knowledge,' p. 255.

APPENDIX VI

LUCRETIUS'S ANTHROPOLOGY

I. THE PROGRESS OF CIVILIZATION.

GUYAU holds that the notion of progress in humanity is in antagonism to the religious idea, and is implied in a naturalistic system. It does not appear in Plato, Socrates, nor, until Seneca, in the Stoics. Most religions place at the beginning of things an Omnipotent Power fashioning the world. In such case the world cannot be conceived as imperfect in its origin, but rather the more divine the younger it is. But where religion is ignored, any theory of the world must be based on a belief in Evolution, in a slow progress upward from a primitive chaos. Therefore, when man appears in the Kosmos, he cannot be conceived as at the stage of civilization where now we find him : his intelligence must develop gradually, his moral sense must grow purer, and Society must come into birth. The only hypothesis which excludes the miraculous is that of a gradual transformation, step by step—*pedetemptim*, as Lucretius says. Epicurus was one of the rare thinkers of antiquity who believed man susceptible of progress. (Such thinkers were hardly so few as Guyau assumes.)[1]

Lucretius has given us a minute analysis of the successive stages of human progress.[2] He begins with primi-

---

[1] Note the liberties which Guyau takes with the text of Epicurus (Diog. L., x. 75). *E.g.*, after τὴν φύσιν he inserts τῶν ἀνθρώπων, etc. (' La Morale d'Épicure,' 1884, p. 158).

[2] v. 925-1457. Possibly Lucretius may here be more than usually independent of Epicurus. The passage is quite evidently

tive man, entirely without instruments, naked, not even
knowing how to cover himself with skins of beasts, and
uttering inarticulate cries. These early men were more
strongly built than we, larger of bone and stronger of
muscle, more endurant of cold and heat. They practised
no tillage, but fed on fruits, which the earth then bore
larger and more plenteous than now. They lived in war-
fare with the animals, flying before the larger and fiercer
ones, but they pursued and made prey of the smaller,
attacking them with showers of stones and with clubs.[1]
From storms or rain they would shelter in woods or caves.
They wandered like beasts with no fixed home, throwing
themselves on the ground wherever night overtook them,
and covering themselves with leaves and boughs. It is
not true, however, that, when the sun sank, they would
call for it with loud wailings. (Lucretius seems to refer
here to some old tradition.) Men were accustomed to see
night follow day, and had no fear but that the sun would
rise again. They dreaded not night, but the wild beasts,
which might disturb them in their lairs.

At this stage men closely resembled the brutes : they
had neither laws nor government : each man lived for
himself alone, and made booty of whatever he could carry
off. From this state men emerged in consequence of
three great discoveries : ' they got for themselves huts
and skins and fire.'[2] If you ask the origin of the last, it
was either lightning or the friction of trees rubbing against
each other. Cooking they were taught by the action of
the sun, seeing that things were softened and made mellow
by the action of its heat. On these discoveries followed
the institution of the family, and man and woman began
to reside under a common roof.

---

an unfinished draught. Munro and Lachman both hold that
1091-1160 is a subsequent addition by the poet : ' These three
paragraphs have no connection with the context either before
or after '; he returns again and again to points already treated.

[1] Apparently for the sake of food, since at this stage Lucretius
has said they did not use skins.

[2] v. 1011.

Apparently not till after this did language come into existence. Nature and need prompted it. It came in by instinct, like that by which the calf butts before his horns are grown. It is absurd to fancy that any one man could have invented it, and fixed on certain sounds to represent certain things. How, indeed, could any one man force others to learn these sounds ? The infant makes a prelude to language when he points with his finger to certain things. As dogs, horses, birds, use certain cries to express different feelings—anger, affection, play—so men use their powers of tongue and voice to denote different things by different sounds. As language originally expressed individual feelings and thoughts, words for given things would at times differ in the same nation. Later, however, men would agree to denote each thing by one uniform name. Still later men of intelligence would introduce terms to denote things not perceived by the senses.[1]

'The first arms or implements were hands, nails, and teeth, stones, and likewise branches broken from the woods, and also flame and fire as soon as these had become known. Later the stoutness of iron and copper were discovered. The use of copper was known before that of iron, since it is easier to work and more abundant.'[2] Metals were first made known from observing masses of melted ore after forests had been on fire. When they saw the shining lumps of metal taking the shape of the hollows in the ground into which they had run, it occurred to them that by the use of heat metal might be cast into any form, and might also be hammered to a sharp edge. Copper, from its ductility, was then more valued than gold or silver, which could not stand being wrought.[3] By slow degrees iron took the place of copper both for ploughs and swords. The science of anthropology confirms Lucretius here.

With the knowledge of fire and the metals all human

---

[1] So Epicurus explains in his letter (Diog. L., x. 75, 76).
[2] v. 1281-1288.
[3] v. 1241-1280.

industries advanced. ' Garments of twisted material,'[1] says Lucretius, ' were in use before woven clothing. Woven stuff came in after iron, because the web is woven by help of iron,' and in no other way can such polished implements be made as the loom requires. These instruments were invented and first used by men, who are more ingenious and skilful than women. But the rugged countrymen so upbraided them that they yielded this lighter task to the female sex.

Civil society developed in the same gradual way. The art of music arose out of the imitation of birds' song. The first musical instrument was the pipe, which was suggested by the wind whistling through hollow reeds, and by degrees the art of music grew. The measuring of time was taught by the stars. Men who excelled others in intellect built towns and strongholds, and made themselves kings, and divided lands among their followers in proportion to their capacity. Strength and beauty gave eminence to individuals. Writing was not discovered till late : hence we can rely only on our reason to tell us how men lived in those early times. Then poetry, painting, sculpture, came in along with all the elegancies of life. ' All these things practice, along with the experience of the never-tiring mind, taught men by slow degrees, as they advanced, step by step. Thus Time by degrees draws on each several thing into view, and reason raises it up into the borders of light.'[2]

Pedetemptim progredientis. This is Lucretius's view of all human progress—a gradual growth.

---

[1] ' Nexilis ante fuit vestis quam textile tegmen '—not, I think, as Munro renders, ' garments tied on '—*i.e.*, skins. Nexilis answers to κασωτῶν in Diogenes of Œnoanda (§ 24, Usener) : ἐσθήτων στρεπτῶν μὲν οὔπω, κασωτῶν δ' ἴσως ἢ ὁποίων οὖν. *Cf.* Hesychius, κάσσον, 'a thick, coarse garment '; κασαῖ, ' horse-rugs of felt,' in Xenophon, ' Cyrop.,' viii. 3.

[2] ' Sic unumquidque paulatim protrahit ætas
In medium ratioque in luminis erigit oras.'

Compare Diog. Œn., § 24, εἶτα δὲ προβαίνων ὁ χρόνος ταῖς ἐπινοίαις αὐτῶν ἢ τῶν μετ' αὐτοὺς ἐνέβαλεν καὶ τὸν ἴστον.

On this subject Diogenes of Œnoanda has preserved the opinions of Epicurus more fully in some details than any other writing we have. He has preserved for us Epicurus's express rejection of the popular mythology, which derived both speech and the arts from the gods. Neither Athena nor any other deity taught men weaving, nor any of the other arts : it was Time that brought them in, he says, ' for necessity and the accidents that occur in course of time brought them all to birth.'[1] Speech arose because ' the men who sprang from the earth ' uttered sounds of themselves. It was not Hermes who taught them, as some say in their conspicuous folly, nor must we believe the philosophers, who assert that speech was the result of a convention or of the teaching of any one man. ' That is more absurd than any absurdity.'

Lucretius's picture of human progress is drawn with breadth and largeness. Such lines as

' Circum se foliis ac frondibus involventes,'

or

' Tum Venus in silvis jungebat corpora amantum,'

show the true Lucretian touch. No other poet could have given us, each in a single line, such pictures which carry us at once far back from Rome and its luxury to a simpler world—as Victor Hugo comments on the last verse, ' The forest is Nature.'[2] An able writer has said that there is no chance of another poem like that of Lucretius being written now. ' Modern science and modern philosophy are of too close a texture to allow anything of the kind. What poetic fire and skill of expression could put into poetry the Scholia and Corollaries of Spinoza or the Categories of Kant ?'[3] But there is one science in which Lucretius, had he lived now, would have found the material for a noble epic. The story of the rise of man on the earth would have fascinated him. The

---

[1] πάσας γὰρ ἐγέννησαν αἱ χρεῖαι καὶ περιπτώσεις μετὰ τοῦ χρόνου, § 24. Cf. πάντων τὴν χρείαν αὐτὴν διδάσκαλον γένεσθαι τοῖς ἀνθρώποις (Diodorus, i. 8, 9)—a genuine Epicurean maxim.

[2] ' William Shakespeare,' Book II., chap. ii.

[3] Dr. W. W. Ireland, in his notice of the present book in the *Journal of Mental Science*, January, 1908, pp. 138-141.

wealth of gathered details with which Anthropology can now fill in his own prescient outline ; the process which prepared the earth as it gradually emerged from the ice for man to spread over it ; how man fought with the beasts, holding his own against them with his poor bow and flint-headed arrows ; his progress upwards from the cavern, in the tenancy of which he succeeded the bear and the hyena ; his advances in tools and weapons ; his strange customs, beliefs, and religious rites ; the beginnings of art, when the cave-man scratched with flint on bone or ivory his rough pictures of elk or mammoth ; the feeble first flowers of literature, when round the fire they told stories of fairies and giants and brave hunters— the whole subject would have suited his genius, and he would have treated it with profound sympathy.

How, then, was the naked, half-beast primitive man transformed into the law-abiding citizen ? Self-interest, Epicurus says, led him to join with others in a compact to keep the laws, and was a sufficient motive to constrain him to do so. Whence, then, came to the savage his sense of right and wrong, vague, distorted, but assuredly present ? Did the steadfast stars overhead implant it in his breast ? We need not inquire into this, Epicurus assures us, seeing that these distinctions are only a convention.

II. THE DOCTRINE OF THE ' SOCIAL CONTRACT ' IN EPICURUS AND LUCRETIUS.

' Tunc et amicitiam cœperunt jungere aventes
Finitimi inter se nec lædere nec violari,
Et pueros commendarunt muliebreque sæclum,
Vocibus et gestu cum balbe significarent
Imbecillorum esse æcum miserier omnis
Nec tamen omnimodis poterat concordia gigni,
Sed bona magnaque pars servabat fœdera caste :
Aut genus humanum jam tum foret omne peremptum
Nec potuisset adhuc perducere sæcla propago.'

v. 1019-1027.

The first two lines are a translation of Epicurus's saying which is quoted below ; *fœdera* (1025) answers to Epi-

curus's συνθῆκαι or σύμβολον.[1] Munro holds that *vocibus*
. . . *balbe* means inarticulate sounds or cries, in accordance with Lucretius's theory of the origin and slow
development of language. Thus, even before they have
learned to speak, men agree by means of signs to live in
peace with one another.

On this doctrine Epicurus anticipated the teaching of
Hobbes and Rousseau, and no doubt influenced both. A
mutual agreement to obey laws for the common interest
is the principle on which he holds society to be based.
Thus he says : ' Natural justice is a covenant of utility
with a view to avoid injuring and being injured.'[1] ' For
those animals which are unable to make agreements not
to injure or be injured no such thing as justice or injustice
exists. The same holds for those nations which are either
unable or unwilling to make such contracts.' ' Justice
has no independent existence ' apart from such contracts.
' Injustice is not intrinsically bad,' except for the fear of
punishment which accompanies it.[2]

In consenting to obey the laws, no one has the interest
of others in view, but merely his own. ' The laws are
established for the sake of the wise, not that they may
not commit injustice, but that they may not suffer it.'[3]

From the moment that any law or restriction is recognized as for the interest of society it becomes just, but so
soon as ever such a law ceases to be for the common interest, from that time it ceases to be just.[4] Those who
live together and obey the laws cease to have any fear of
their neighbours : they feel mutual confidence, and enjoy
the conditions necessary for happiness.[5]

Thus, says Guyau, human societies ' have built themselves up gradually by an accumulation of habits, of
customs, by the gradual accommodation of individuals

[1] τὸ τῆς φύσεως δίκαιον ἐστι σύμβολον τοῦ συμφέροντος εἰς τὸ μὴ
βλάπτειν μήδε βλάπτεσθαι (Diog. L., x. 150).
[2] *Ibid.*, x. 150-151 ; see also sayings 47 and 48, quoted in
vol. i., p. 349.
[3] Stobæus 'Floril.,' 43, 139.
[4] Diog. L., x. 152.   [5] *Ibid.*, x. 154.

one to the other.   The ideas of justice, of right, of charity,
and of philanthropy, far from having produced society,
flow from society itself ; far from explaining it, they are
explained by it.'[1]

Guyau comments thus : ' It is a long way from this
ideal of mutual fellowship and confidence to the primitive
and natural state of man.   According to Epicurus, as according to Hobbes, men in the state of Nature behave like
wolves to one another (*l'homme est un loup pour l'homme*).
" Without contracts and laws," Metrodorus used to say,
" we should devour one another."   Epicurus is open to
the charge of transforming wolves into lambs rather
speedily.   No doubt the Epicurean wise man who has
extinguished within himself every violent desire and
every disturbing passion will be able to discern that it
is more for his interest to observe the social contract
than to violate it.   Unfortunately, Epicurean society,
like every other, is not composed exclusively of wise men.
In the eyes of those who are not wise, will the social
force be sufficient of itself to render a conventional justice
born from a contract of mutual interest respected and
inviolable ?   This difficulty is common to the system of
Epicurus, and to all utilitarian systems.   It is not the
place here to discuss its importance.'[2]

[1] ' La Morale d'Épicure,' p. 286.
[2] *Ibid.*, p. 152.   See also the second part of Guyau's well-
known work, ' Morale Anglaise Contemporaine.'

APPENDIX VII

LUCRETIUS'S ARGUMENT FOR FREE-WILL (II. 284-287)—IS THERE A DIFFICULTY HERE?—'NECESSITY' IN NATURE AND FREEDOM IN MAN

> 'Quare in seminibus quoque idem fateare necessest,
> Esse aliam præter plagas et pondera causam
> Motibus, unde hæc est nobis innata potestas,
> De nilo quoniam fieri nil posse videmus.'
>
> ii. 284-287.

'WHEREFORE, in the case of atoms, too,[1] you must admit the same—namely, that besides blows and weights, there is another cause for [their] movements,[2] whence this power of free action has been begotten in us, since we see that nothing can come from nothing.'

In these lines Lucretius sums up his reasoning on the most characteristic and weighty point of his master's system. The whole passage (ll. 251-293) is most closely reasoned. Not a word is thrown away. When we come to this sentence, however, we pause, and for a time are bewildered. Has not Lucretius told us that the atoms have two motions, a perpendicular downward motion,

---

[1] The force of *quoque* must not be forgotten. It refers to the preceding illustrations of free-will action in men and animals. It means ' in atoms as well as in human beings.'

[2] Is *motibus* ' for their movements '—*i.e.*, for the movements of the atoms—or ' for our movements '? ' For their movements,' though less plausible, is the most consistent with Lucretius's argument. He is reasoning from men to atoms, and applies his famous axiom *ex nihilo nihil* in a very bold and forcible way : ' If men can move at will, then the atoms which they come from must be able to move at will too.'

and a slight swerving from the perpendicular, but for which they would never have come into contact ? This swerving produces collisions among the atoms or ' blows ' —*plagæ*. He has proved that blows could not have been but for declination. How, then, does he say that, in addition to weight and blows, which latter can only be caused by declination, we must admit the existence of declination ? Is Lucretius unmindful or inconsistent ? For does not this passage imply that *plagæ* exist apart from declination, and before it comes into play ? Not by any means, we think. But the commentators certainly do not assist us to master the thought of this passage. In the first place, Cicero (referring possibly, his language leads us to think, to this very passage, which he may have read, and, if so, certainly misunderstood) has contrived to paraphrase the subject-matter of it in such a way as peculiarly to mislead anyone who compares this passage of Lucretius with Cicero's words in ' De Fato.' He says : ' Epicurus declinatione atomi vitari fati necessitatem putat : itaque tertius quidam motus oritur extra pondus et plagam quum declinat atomus intervallo minimo ' (' De Fato,' x.). Cicero here states the doctrine of Epicureanism in a singularly careless and inexact way, and his unqualified mode of applying the phrase, ' a third kind of motion,' seems to have misled all later commentators. In his note on the passage, Mr. Munro makes no reference to the difficulty, but in his abstract of ll. 251-293 he gives the argument thus : ' While the weight, then, of atoms enables *them* sometimes to withstand the external force of blows, it is only this declination of atoms at quite uncertain times and places which gives the mind its freedom of action '; and again, on l. 288 : ' Lucretius, too, like Cicero, assigns the freedom of the will as the chief proof of the necessity of this third motion.' Again, M. Guyau (' La Morale d'Épicure,' p. 77), commenting on the passage, says : ' There exist, then, according to Epicurus (and the testimony of Cicero here confirms that of Lucretius), three causes of motion,

each profounder and more inward than the other : blows
which are at the same time exterior and fatal (*fatal*),
weight which is interior but appears still fatal, and finally
Free-will, which is at the same time interior and free.'
And (p. 78, note) : ' Cicero [in the passage above quoted]
is entirely in agreement with Lucretius.'

Lucretius's reasoning becomes at once clear when we
see that in this passage he is speaking *only* with reference
to the human soul.   He here assumes the existence of the
world, as originally caused by Declination, and discusses
the freedom of the will as a question entirely apart.   He
passes suddenly from the outer world, governed by necessity in the form of natural laws (the consequence of *pondus*
and *plagæ*), to the soul of man.   Lucretius is here insisting
on *the freedom of the human will amid the vast mechanism
of Nature which surrounds it*.   Man could not be free
unless there exist in all atoms, and therefore in the
atoms of his soul also, a principle apart from the *pondus*
and *plagæ* which govern the world without.   This power
of the soul-atoms to decline at will exists also in all
atoms, but in the inorganic world he conceives it to be
nullified.   In the world of Nature Epicurus knows of
only two[1] causes of motion : first, Gravity, causing a
perpendicular, and, secondly, Declination, causing a
swerving motion, which produces *plagæ* or ' collisions.'
(It is *plagæ* alone which, though there is no authority
for so denoting it, might deserve to be called a third
motion.)   Strictly speaking, Cicero's phrase, ' a third kind
of motion ' (as applied by him, and followed by all subsequent writers), is misleading.   Free-will exists in all
atoms.   In the soul-atoms it is active, and can originate
motion ; but in the atoms composing dead matter it is
potential only, and can never be ' a cause of motion.'
As we have already pointed out,[2] Epicurus seems to have

[1] So far as we know, no ancient authority speaks of a third.
Cf. Aetius, ' De Plac. Ph.,' i. 23, 4 : Ἐπίκουρος δύο εἴδη τῆς
κινήσεως τὸ κατὰ στάθμην καὶ τὸ κατὰ παρέγκλισιν.   This sentence
is repeated at i. 12.

[2] See above, pp. 86-7.

assumed that the power of Declination, though still existing in the atoms, practically disappears after these atoms
have combined to form matter. Various counteracting
causes tend to nullify it. Besides, Free-will is proportionally a far feebler power in gross matter than it is in
the soul, and is far more easily held in check.

Epicurus speaks of no third cause of motion in the
outer world. *It is only for the mind*, amid the necessity
of Nature, which is twofold, *that a third cause of motion
exists*—namely, the Free-will of the soul-atoms. This
important paragraph can be understood aright only when
we realize that in it Lucretius sharply distinguishes between the world of Nature, which is absolutely governed
by necessity—that is to say, by natural law—and the
mind of man. His system,

> ' Binding Nature fast in fate,
> Leaves free the human will.'

I have always found a difficulty in this passage, which I
cannot think entirely of my own creation.

APPENDIX VIII

EPICURUS'S DOCTRINE OF 'THE VERACITY OF THE SENSES'

THE first principle of the Epicurean theory of knowledge is that all sensations are of themselves reliable. If error arises from these, it arises in our interpretation of them, since, if we are to gain any knowledge from sensations, they must be interpreted by our reason. We see a tower a mile away which appears round ; experience leads us to correct this by a nearer view from different points, and we then find it to be square. Reason alone can decide on this process, and tell us when and how far we require to correct one sense-impression by another. Therefore, in reality, it is reason, and not sensation, which carries the highest authority.

Giussani endeavours at some length to prove that Epicurus is not inconsistent here, but, after careful study of his reasoning, I cannot admit its force or its logic. In the following passage[1] Dr. Brieger has admirably stated the objection to Giussani's defence of Epicurus :

' How, then, am I to distinguish the false interpretation of a sensation from the true ? The " veracity of the senses " laid down by Epicurus is of no value for the knowledge of Nature, because it indicates only the agreement of the sense-impression with its direct cause (in the case of visual impression, for example, with the sensory image), not its agreement with the object. This was first

---

[1] ' Jahresbericht über die Fortschritte der Class. Alterthumsw.,' 1900, ' Zweite Abtheilung,' p. 2.

proved by Tohte,[1] and Giussani does not succeed in refuting the charge. He refers to the twenty-fourth cardinal maxim without quoting the passage, and on the following page he says : " Not the reason, but the repeated attempt under willed conditions, has in different cases to decide whether an image accurately renders itself merely, or the object from which it proceeds."[2]   Therewith he has the key in his hand, but he does not use it. What else is it than the Reason which decides whether a second observation is to be preferred ? The deceiving sense-perception cannot itself tell that it is unreliable. Now Giussani repeatedly says that the Reason is nothing more than a movement of the atoms, a secondary one which is dependent on the movements accompanying the sense-impressions, and is called forth by them, and it must certainly be this if Epicurus were quite consistent here. Consequently a movement which is dependent on sense-perception must decide whether one single sense-impression is reliable or not. Giussani does not succeed in disproving that we have here a reasoning in a circle.'

Giussani goes on to explain that Epicurus held Reason to be ' nothing else than an atomic motion originally provoked by sensation, which is born of sensation and is, in a fashion, nothing but elaborated sensation.' ' If, owing to the scarcity of authorities,' he continues, ' we do not know how Epicurus made Reason to be derived from the senses, this would not give us the right to affirm that Epicurus may not have attended to explaining the matter to himself and to others.'[3]   But the absence of negative evidence does not amount to proof positive of a statement.

[1] ' Epikurs Kriterien der Wahrheit,' p. 10.

[2] ' Secundo Epicuro, non già il λόγος ma la rinnovata esperienza nelle volute condizioni (thus Giussani explains the term ἐπιμαρτύρησις, " confirmation of experience," κύριαι δόξαι, 24) ha da decidere nei diversi casi se un εἴδωλον rappresenta fedelmente solo sè stesso o anche l'oggetto da cui muove ' (' Studi,' p. lvii).

[3] ' Studi,' pp. lvii, lviii.

Our knowledge of facts depends, according to Giussani,
on sensation plus the repetition of the given sensation
' under willed conditions '—that is to say, if I think my
first impression that a tower is round not reliable enough,
I decide to repeat my impression, and verify it by viewing
the tower nearer and from different points. But what
decides me to do this ? Giussani correctly says it is my
will (*voluti condizioni*). But will implies an act of reasoning, judging from previous experience of objects seen at
a distance. It is idle to try to get rid of this mental
exercise by calling it ' experience.' Giussani has by no
means cleared Epicurus from the charge, ' If with Epicurus
the authority of reason depends upon the authority of
sensation, how, then, can reason dare to contradict and
overrule sensation ?'

In a sense every sensation is true. The oar that seems
broken in the water is an actual sense-picture of the oar
due to the refraction of light. But according to our
πρόληψις of an oar, all oars are straight, and our reason
tells us that in this case the sense-picture has somehow
become modified. The dragon seen by the madman comes
from an actual image which has sprung up somehow in his
diseased brain. The sane man might also see such a
dragon when recovering from a fever or in a moment of
hallucination, but he would not believe in its existence.
He compares it with the results of his previous sane
experience, and rejects it. It follows that a true sensation
may be a false mental picture.

APPENDIX IX

THE INVOCATION TO VENUS

A DIFFERENT explanation, which does not reduce the Invocation either to a parody or to a concession, is offered by a French writer, M. Martha.[1] According to him we have here an allegory : the goddess Venus is a personification of the great law of life and reproduction in Nature— the sovereign law which rules the world. ' These beautiful images, borrowed from the national religion, enclose a profession of faith and a fundamental doctrine of Epicureanism.' As the poet proceeds and prays to Venus to beg from Mars, her lover, peace for the Romans, in this Lucretius more and more confounds Venus with the mythic ancestress of the Roman race—but this is a simple play of imagination. No mythological tone need necessarily be seen in the address ' Æneadum genetrix.' It is probably here but a title of Venus, and of all her names the one dearest to Roman ears. Lucretius did not believe that she was ancestress of the Romans, and, had he been a modern author, would not have used the phrase.

Martha (Appendix, p. 358) makes the suggestion—a very natural one—that in this beautiful picture Lucretius has reproduced some statuary group of Venus soothing Mars. It is probable that the two were frequently represented in the attitude here described. Certain phrases, such as ' tereti cervice reflexa,' suggest this, he says.

The notion that Venus and Mars are merely two alle-

---

[1] 'Le Poème de Lucrèce,' 1873, pp. 100-106.

gorical figures, Love and Strife, or the motions of destruction and renewal ever at work in Nature, in spite of Sellar's
eloquent vindication, appears artificial, or at least without
sufficient evidence. Bockemüller (in his edition of
Lucretius, 1874, part i., p. 10) holds Venus to be a
mere personification of natural law, but offers a novel
explanation of the passage. According to him, Lucretius's
petition for peace is directed in reality, and under cover
of the figures Venus and Mars, to the newly-wedded pair,
Julia and Pompey, who were for Romans of that period
' the universally acknowledged representatives of super-
sensual power.' ' Julia (Julus, Æneas, Venus) = Venus,
and Pompeius M. = Mars.' It was, I believe, Martha
who first called attention to the fact, as explaining this
passage, that the Roman Emperor and his consort were
often represented in statuary under the guise of Mars
and Venus.

There is certainly a strange contrast between the Venus
of the opening lines, the world-spirit filling earth and air,
and the mythological Venus depicted in the close of the
same paragraph in a love scene with Mars. ' The former,'
say the critics, ' is only an allegory, and the latter a mere
poetic personification. The poet did not trouble himself
about the contradiction.' But do we know enough
about that strange Epicurean theology to be certain as to
either of these suppositions ?

We must beware of attributing to Lucretius ideas which
are foreign to him. For instance, Symonds says that
Lucretius, ' dropping the phraseology of atoms, void,
motion or chance, spoke at times of Nature as endowed
with reason and a will,' but no one of the passages which
he quotes (v. 186, 811, 846) appears to have this
meaning. ' Nature,' as Lucretius uses the word, means
but the laws of Nature, the habits of the world—that is
all. Yet it is true that, having discarded the old Divine
agencies, the notion of Nature as a new self-working power
might easily come.

APPENDIX X

THE DOCTRINE OF ISONOMIA—ITS BEARING UPON EPI-
CUREAN THEOLOGY — SCOTT'S INTERPRETATION OF
THE DOCTRINE — HIS THEORY ADOPTED AND DE-
VELOPED FURTHER BY GIUSSANI—THEIR THEORY
INCONSISTENT WITH THE LEADING DOCTRINES OF
EPICURUS.

IN a long chapter entitled 'The Epicurean Gods and the
Doctrine of Isonomia,' Giussani discusses the doctrine
of 'Isonomia'—that is to say, on the 'Balance of Forces
in the universe' as bearing upon Epicurus's theology.
A singular theory has been propounded on this subject
by Scott, which Giussani adopts and develops further.
Both scholars find a very essential connection between
these doctrines. I have examined their theory at some
length in the *Classical Review* (December, 1902).

After the passage on the Epicurean Godhead quoted in
the next Appendix, p. 140, Cicero adds a further argument,
which he states very briefly, for the Divine existence.

'Summa vero vis infinitatis et magna ac diligenti con-
templatione dignissima est, in qua intellegi necesse est
eam esse naturam ut omnia omnibus paribus paria re-
spondeant. Hanc ἰσονομίαν appellat Epicurus, id est
æquabilem tributionem. Ex hac igitur illud efficitur, si
mortalium tanta multitudo sit, esse immortalium non
minorem,[1] et si quæ interimant innumerabilia sint, etiam

---

[1] Zeller says, 'The words from "et si quæ interimant" to the
end belong to Cicero only, for Epicurus cannot have described
his idle Gods as Beings who preserve the world' ('Stoics, Epi-

ea quæ conservent infinita esse debere ' (' De Natura Deorum,' i. 50).

' Surely the mighty power of the infinite universe is most worthy of our great and earnest contemplation ; we must understand that the constitution of the infinite whole is such that all its parts are exactly balanced one against the other.[1] This is called by Epicurus " Isonomia "— that is to say, " an equal distribution " of things. From this principle it results[2] that, if there is so great a number of mortals, there must be no smaller number of immortals, and if the forces which destroy are innumerable, those which preserve things in being must also be innnumerable.'

This passage is criticized by the Academic disputant, Cotta, at § 109. Cotta refuses to grant to Velleius that, if the constant stream of Divine images is due to the infinity of matter, he is justified in inferring from the same cause the eternity of the Gods.

' Quomodo enim probas continenter imagines ferri ? aut, si continenter, quomodo æternæ ? " Innumerabilitas," inquit, " suppeditat atomorum." Num eadem ergo ista faciet ut sint omnia sempiterna ? Confugis ad æquilibritatem (sic enim ἰσονομίαν, si placet, appellemus) et dicis, quoniam sit natura mortalis, immortalem etiam esse oportere. Isto modo, quoniam homines mortales sunt, sint aliqui immortales, et quoniam nascuntur in terra, nascantur in aqua. " Et quia sunt quæ interimant, sunt quæ conservent ?" Sint sane, sed ea conservent quæ sunt : deos istos esse non sentio.'

We find the doctrine stated by Cicero expressed in more limited application, but in much more explicit terms, in Lucretius,[3] though not under the name of ' Isonomia.' No other writer refers to the subject.

---

cureans, and Sceptics,' p. 442, note, in German edition of 1881). Brieger has, I believe, somewhere expressed an opinion that the doctrine stated in this passage (§ 50) does not come from Epicurus himself, but was added to his system by some later Epicurean.

[1] We follow Mayor's rendering.
[2] Whose inference is this, Epicurus's or Cicero's ?
[3] ii. 569-580 ; also v. 381-396.

The doctrine has a broad and simple meaning, which has been thus stated by Munro : ' In the universe of things death and destruction are evenly balanced by life and production.' This statement covers all the definite references to this tenet in Lucretius.

Cicero, however, gives us a wider application of the doctrine, not merely as a Balance of opposing Forces, but as a pairing of opposite things, one of which implies the other. Thus, mortality implies immortality : if so many mortals exist, there must be an equal number of immortals ; if life is produced on land, living things must be produced on water too (§ 109), and so on.

Scott's explanation is that in our world the processes of growth and decay go on alternately, but that outside the worlds in the *intermundia* the *motus auctifici* and the *motus exitiales* must work simultaneously, and result in the immortality of such beings as there exist. Giussani follows Scott, but holds that his theory ' is not the whole truth.' The cause of the death of any living creature is the ' persistence ' of the matter of its body. This matter may be suddenly dispersed at any moment by an accident. Even in the *intermundia* the gods may be exposed to such fatal injury. The only security for their immortality is ' that their matter should be absolutely non-persistent.' Such a condition his ' cascade-like ' Gods supply. The processes of waste and gain in their bodies must therefore be ' instantaneous '!

Both scholars build their surprising theories on the foundation of Cicero's line or two at § 49, repeated with slight variation at § 109 of the ' De Natura Deorum,' a corrupt passage of Diogenes and a few clauses and shreds of sentences from Philodemus being also twisted in highly uncritical fashion to support their view. Cicero has given us an admirable account of Epicurean ethics, but his whole exposition of the details of Epicurus's theology is too vague and hasty, not to say contemptuous ; the data he gives are far too slight and too unsteady to justify the dogmatic tone which the Italian scholar adopts.

Until we know much more about it, any interpretation of the doctrine of Isonomia, except in its broad meaning of a ' Balance of Forces,' can only claim the value of an inference of the most tentative kind.

The consequences implied in the infinity of matter according to Epicureanism are well understood, and have been fully set forth by various writers. To sustain the *plagæ*, the constant succession of atomic collisions and resulting constant upstreaming of fresh atoms to feed the world and maintain the balance between preserving and destroying forces, matter must be infinite.[1] As of the world, so also the continued existence of the Gods depends on the infinity of matter. There is nothing new in this. But why should Giussani re-label all these doctrines with the title ' Isonomia ' ?

[1] See Volume I., Chapter V., pp. 109-115.

APPENDIX XI

CICERO ON THE EPICUREAN GODS — THEORIES OF
LACHELIER AND SCOTT—WAS THERE AN ESOTERIC
EPICUREAN THEOLOGY ?

IT is now time to examine the theory of the Epicurean
Gods propounded by Giussani in the chapter of his
' Studi ' discussed in the last Appendix. The theory he
propounds here was first set forth by Lachelier[1] and Scott,[2]
and is further developed by Giussani himself. His own
view is ingenious and novel, and is worth examining.
In order to do justice to it, the various difficult and
corrupt texts bearing on Epicurean theology must be
considered and compared.

Epicurus must have treated the subject of the Gods at
length, but evidently in a way which too much taxed the
patience of his opponents, who may have some excuse for
not thoroughly grasping his point of view. Light was
first thrown on the subject by Schoemann in his admirable
paper on the 'Theology of Epicurus,'[3] and Mr. Mayor, in his
excellent commentary on Cicero's ' De Natura Deorum,'
has grappled fairly and fully with all the difficulties of the
question, and has left the subject much clearer than he
found it.

Lachelier's theory is based upon a passage of Cicero

---

[1] *Revue de Philologie*, 1877, p. 264.

[2] ' The Physical Constitution of the Epicurean Gods,' *Journal
of Philology*, 1883, pp. 212-247. Mr. Scott has here worked out
the theory with great learning and ingenuity.

[3] 'De Epicuri Theologia,' Opuscula, vol. iv., pp. 336-359.
Hirzel also discusses the subject with his usual acuteness, ' Unter-
suchungen zu Cicero's Philosophischen Schriften,' part i., 1877.

which is so vague in expression that the interpretation
is almost hopelessly difficult. Schoemann says that
Cicero himself could not have understood what he wrote
here. All scholars agree that Cicero is here translating
from a Greek original. It appears to me certain that he
is not merely translating, but also attempting to condense
and give the gist of a passage which baffled his understanding, or probably which he grudged taking the pains
to understand. He begins by referring sarcastically to
Epicurus's definition of the Divine nature as one too subtle
for an average mind to understand, and apologizes for the
briefness with which he is going to set it forth. Probably
every clause of his Latin represents a sentence at least in
the Greek. Cotta, the Academic critic, referring to the
Divine images, says : ' *If you yourselves who defend the
doctrine understood it*, I should then be ashamed to say
I do not understand it ' (§ 109.) Thus Cicero warns us
broadly enough that his account of the subject must be
received with caution.

The passage runs : ' Hæc quamquam et inventa sunt
acutius et dicta subtilius ab Epicuro, quam ut quivis ea
possit agnoscere,[1] tamen fretus intelligentia vestra dissero
brevius quam causa desiderat. Epicurus autem, qui res
occultas et penitus abditas non modo viderit animo, sed
etiam sic tractet, ut manu, docet eam esse vim et naturam
deorum, ut primum non sensu, sed mente cernatur, nec
soliditate quadam neque *eadem* ad numerum *sit*,[2] ut ea,
quæ ille propter firmitatem στερέμνια appellat ; sed,
imaginibus similitudine et transitione[3] perceptis, cum
infinita simillimarum imaginum *series*[4] ex innumerabilibus

---

[1] Not ' too hard for anyone to understand,' but ' for everyone '—*i.e.*, for the average person.

[2] Mayor inserts the words 'eadem . . ., sit.'

[3] *Transitione*. The context would seem to require *continua-
tione*, ' a continued series,' rather than *transitione*. It is only
the continued stream of images which can cause perception :
singly, these images are imperceptible. See Lucretius, iv. 87-89,
104-109, 256 *ff*.

[4] The MSS. read 'species.' I follow Brieger's excellent emendation, which seems almost required by *affluat*. Mayor says

individuis exsistat et ad nos[1] affluat, cum[2] maximis volup-
tatibus in eas imagines mentem intentam infixamque
nostram intellegentiam capere, quæ sit et beata natura
et æterna '[3] (' De Natura Deorum,' i. 49).

The careless scribes who altered *ad nos* first to *ad eos*
and then to *ad deos* have called forth much wasted ingenuity.

Lachelier keeps the reading *ad deos*, and translates as
follows :

' According to Epicurus, the Divine nature is of such a
kind that it is perceived not by the senses, but by thought ;
it has neither the quality of solidity, nor has it numerical
identity, like these things which Epicurus calls στερέμνια
on account of their solidity ; but by the perception of a
series of similar images, when an infinite succession of
images of precisely similar form arises out of the innumerable atoms and flows to the Gods, our mind, intently

---

' *Species* is the technical term to denote the mental impression
produced by the *imagines* : (Div. ii. 137, "nulla species cogitari
potest nisi pulsu imaginum ") ; . . . *affluat* is very suitably used of
the series *imaginum* flowing in upon the mind, but less suitably
of the *species* which springs up within the mind itself.' If Cicero
wrote ' species,' it would only be in keeping with the vagueness
of the whole passage.

[1] The MSS. have *deos* ; one or two *eos*. The correction is due
to Lambinus.

[2] Giussani changes *cum* to *tum*, and makes this word the
beginning of a new sentence (' Studi Lucreziani,' p. 259).

[3] Schoemann reads ' quæ sit et beatæ naturæ et æternæ ' ;
but the words as they stand give the necessary meaning—' what
that being is which is at once blessed and eternal.' Zeller's
comment on § 49 is as follows : ' These words appear to mean
that ideas of the Gods are not formed in the same manner as our
ideas of other solid bodies—namely, by a number of similar
pictures from the same object striking our senses (Diog. L.,
x. 95)—but by single pictures emanating from innumerable
divine individuals, all so much alike that they leave behind
them the impressions of perfect happiness and immortality.'
Zeller translates *individuis* ' göttliche Individuen,' but there
seems to be no instance of the word bearing the meaning of
' a person,' either human or divine.

fixed upon these images, comes to apprehend the nature of a being at once blessed and eternal.'

The conclusion is forced upon me that Cicero has confused the word σώματα, which he found in his original in the sense 'the Divine bodies,' with σώματα in its common sense, 'atoms.' He repeats this misunderstanding later at § 105, where Cotta, the critic of the Academy, repeats his opponent's definition of the Divine being, before criticizing it, in the same order as at § 49, while in his final clause *mens nostra* confirms us in reading *ad nos*.

'Sic enim dicebas speciem Dei percipi cogitatione, non sensu, nec esse in ea ullam soliditatem neque eandem ad numerum permanere, eamque esse ejus visionem ut similitudine et transitione cernatur, neque deficiat unquam ex infinitis corporibus similium accessio, ex eoque fieri ut in hæc intenta mens nostra beatam illam naturam et sempiternam putet.'

(*Similitudine* and *transitione* imply the word *imaginum*, which must be supplied with *similium*.)

How could *imagines* be produced from 'atoms'? *Imagines* can only come from a 'thing,' here a form in human shape. Is it possible that the text at § 49 has become corrupt, and that for *ex innumerabilibus individuis* we ought to read *ex innumerabilibus corporibus divinis*, the words *divinus* and *individuus* being at times confused in the MSS.? Immediately after this passage (in § 50) Cicero shows that the number of immortal beings is as countless as that of mortals. It is more probable that we have to deal at § 49 with a careless translation than with a corruption, but it seems not too bold to say that Cicero's Greek original there had 'from the countless Divine bodies.' Doubtless the never-ceasing flow of Divine images presupposes an infinity of matter, but it presupposes still more directly an infinite number of Gods.

Epicurus uses the word στερέμνια to denote 'solid bodies.'[1] It could not be applied, for example, to the

[1] Diog. L., x. 50.

εἴδωλα, which are films having comparatively no depth. Scott says : 'The clause ("ut ea quæ ille propter firmitatem στερέμνια appellat ") would seem to assert that the Gods are of the nature of εἴδωλα rather than of tangible bodies, or are *surfaces* rather than *solids*. And this agrees perfectly with what we are told elsewhere about the *quasi-corpus* of the Gods.' He then quotes Cotta's saying that the Divine bodies have 'nihil concreti, nihil solidi, nihil expressi, nihil eminentis' (§ 75), and says that other contemptuous references by opponents (*e.g.*, i. 123, 'lineamentis dumtaxat extremis, non habitu solido' ; ii. 59, 'monogrammos deos,' 'Gods in outline' ; 'De Div.,' ii. 40, 'deos perlucidos et perflabiles') all suggest beings having *shape* or *outline*, but not *bulk*. The aim of such sarcastic references is by exaggeration to make the Gods of Epicurus a butt for ridicule, so that these phrases cannot be taken literally and used for evidence. If the bodies of the Gods must not be called 'solid,' it is not because they are 'films,' but because their texture is too ethereal.

Scott explains the passage thus : 'The Gods, though material, are not firm and solid like the gross bodies of men and visible things, but of a far finer texture. They have not *numerical* or *material*, but only formal identity ; in other words, the matter of which they are composed, instead of remaining fixed and identically the same through a finite space of time, as is the case with visible and tangible objects, is *perpetually passing away, to be replaced by fresh matter*, the *form* or arrangement of matter alone remaining unchanged. They are formed by perpetual successions of " images " or material films of precisely similar form, which, having arisen (in some unexplained way) out of the infinite atoms dispersed through the universe, stream to a sort of focus, and there, by their meeting, constitute for a moment the being of the Gods ; then, streaming away again in all directions, they pass into the (material) mind of man.'

Scott, following Hirzel, quotes from Aristotle to show

that *nec ad numerum* represents the Greek κατ᾽ ἀριθμὸν as opposed to κατ᾽ εἶδος. The former phrase denotes a thing which is permanently the same in its material substance, like the pond, as opposed to that which changes in matter but remains the same in form alone (ταὐτὸ κατ᾽ εἶδος), like the river. The Divine body is like the river : its matter is absolutely fleeting, but its ' form ' abides.[1]

Brieger's wide knowledge of Epicurean doctrine enables him to criticize Giussani shrewdly here. Brieger, however, accepts his view in part. ' Giussani,' he says, ' compares the Divine body to a waterfall, the appearance of which remains the same, while the water forming it changes every moment. A Being existing in this fashion is immortal if the influx of homogeneous matter does not cease, for every interruption of that which subsists in a constant " Becoming " is without enduring effect, " like a shot fired into a waterfall." That such Beings can exist is testified by Philodemus, περὶ εὐσεβείας (Gomperz, " Hercul. Stud.," p. 110). So far Giussani is undoubtedly right.'[2] The sentence of Philodemus referred to is quite insufficient to justify such a statement ; the interpretations extorted from it differ very widely ; its meaning is simply a riddle.[3] This and other fragments

---

[1] Is not the Platonic term applied in a rather superficial way to such ' Beings ' (?) as these ' river-like ' or, as Giussani calls them, ' waterfall-like ' Gods ?   Plato would have used the term ' Form ' of the river, but never of the water rushing through a single point on the course of that river.   Giussani even thinks it not impossible that ' the Platonic Realism ' may have influenced Epicurus in this part of his theology ! (' Studi,' p. 257, note).   To students of philosophy a surprising opinion indeed ! Two thinkers more hostile, less allied even on any single point, than Plato and Epicurus could not be found.

[2] ' Jahresbericht über die Fortschritte der Class.,' Alterthumsw., 1900, p. 5.

[3] Scott's version, made by dint of transpositions, etc., may be found in *Journal of Philology*, p. 232 ; that of Giussani, who does not adopt these changes, at ' Studi Lucr.,' p. 261. (Giussani's ἀποπλεῖσθαι seems a misprint.)

of Philodemus suggest that Epicureanism had developed
a new terminology since its founder's day.

Another passage in Diog. L., x. 139, is also more or
less corrupt, and almost as vague and difficult to understand as that in Cicero. It is a slipshod comment of his
own which Diogenes adds after the first of the κύριαι δόξαι.

ἐν ἄλλοις δέ φησι τοὺς θεοὺς λόγῳ θεωρητοὺς οὓς
μεν [οὐ μὲν Schoemann] κατ' ἀριθμὸν ὑφεστῶτας, οὓς δὲ
[γνωστοὺς δὲ Schoemann] κατὰ ὁμοέιδειαν ἐκ τῆς συνεχοῦς
ἐπιρρύσεως τῶν ὁμοίων ἐιδώλων ἐπὶ τὸ αὐτὸ ἀποτετελεσμένους
ἀνθρωποειδεῖς.¹

It looks as if both Cicero and Diogenes had been puzzled
by the same original, and had both tried to give its drift
in brief. The slovenly-worded sentence has been supposed
to mean that Epicurus believed in two classes of gods.
Usener, somewhat arbitrarily, omits it as a scholion.
Schoemann's brilliant emendation γνωστοὺς is based on
the principle that the human mind can apprehend the
gods because the substance of both is the same—namely
the finest atoms ; it would mean that the gods ' are
discerned by the mind owing to the likeness of their
substance.'

Mayor accepts the passage as genuine, and thinks it
may refer to an esoteric and an exoteric Epicurean
theology, so that ' we may apparently assume that
Epicurus himself, or some of his followers, acknowledged
a divinity of a more spiritual type, distinct from those
in the *intermundia*. An attentive consideration of
Cicero's language forces on the reader the conclusion that

¹ Hirzel (p. 73) reads οὖς μεν . . . οὖς δὲ, and understands
the words as referring on the one hand to the true Gods who
dwell in the *intermundia*, and on the other to the Divine images.
We know that Democritus did to some extent regard the Divine
εἴδωλα as having a certain independent existence. It may be
due to a remembrance of Democritus that Cicero on two occa-
sions speaks as if, for the moment, he regarded the flying Divine
images as equivalent to Deity and as eternal (' De Natura Deorum,'
i. 109 and ii. 76), but Hirzel puts an extreme strain upon these
mere allusions. Cicero knows well that the Epicurean Gods are
altogether *outside* the world.

there were two distinct systems of theology recognized
in the Epicurean school—one of a more esoteric nature,
taken mainly from their great authority, Democritus, the
other more suited to the popular belief—which two systems
have, not unnaturally, been confounded together by
Cicero.'[1]

There is, however, no reliable evidence for any such
esoteric Epicurean theology.

Any opinion of Edward Zeller's carries such weight as
to deserve recording, whether we accept it or not. His
interpretation of this passage is largely influenced by
Hirzel. He reads οὐ μέντοι instead of οὓς μὲν. After
the remark that Epicurus bases our belief in Divine
existences on the atom-pictures, he adds : ' Only part of
these pictures guarantee to us the actual perception of
Divine Beings, while others are, as we should say, merely
the creations of our fancy, or, as Epicurus would say,
they are merely pictures floating about in the air which
have no material thing actually existing to answer to
them.'[2] We perceive these last because they are like
each other, are in human form, and because a constant
succession of them streams to us. We may compare with
Diogenes' language Cicero's words, ' similitudine et transitione perceptis ' (' De Natura Deorum,' i. 49).

According to Epicurus's sensationalism, not only must
our true conceptions of the Gods arise from pictures, but
our false conceptions of them must also arise from the
perception of εἴδωλα, which do not have actual individuals
behind them. So understood, the sentence of Diogenes
corresponds, if we allow for a misunderstanding of Cicero's,
with Cicero's own account in ' De Natura Deorum,' i. 49.
Both Cicero and Diogenes can only refer, in this explanation, to the Gods of the common people, which do not

[1] On Cicero, ' De Natura Deorum,' i., § 49, pp. 147 (note)
and 148.
[2] The eight lines added in the text in the German edition of
1880, as well as a very long note, are omitted in the English
translation of 1901.

exist κατ' ἀριθμὸν ' as individuals,' though Cicero elsewhere treats it as if it referred to Epicurus's own Gods.

Zeller's interpretation has got to be reckoned with. I
cannot see my way to accept it. How are we to discern
such false Divine images from the real ? Moreover,
Epicurus has no quarrel with the popular notions as to the
form and aspect of the Gods, but merely with our own
false inferences ascribing to Deity the passions and
resentments of men.

Another reference to the Epicurean Gods occurs in the
treatise of the pseudo-Plutarch, ' De Plac. Phil.,' I. vii. 15,
where we are told that Epicurus believed in ' four immortal
elements—the atoms, the void, the infinite universe,
the Likehoods ' (τὰς ὁμοιότητας). Some blundering
scribe explains the last word in a gloss as referring to
Anaxagoras's elements. (Usener treats the whole clause
as a hostile comment—*additamentum malevoli*). In any
case this fourth element must refer to the Gods. Is it
possible that the words *similitudine perceptis* and other
phrases as to ' likeness ' which so often recur in this
reference in Cicero, Diogenes and Philodemus represent
in their Greek original the term αἱ ὁμοιότητες, which
Cicero may have misunderstood ? The term may originally have denoted much the same thing as *imagines*, but
used in a restrictive sense to mean ' the Divine Likenesses,'
and next the Gods themselves.

Until we can find the original which Cicero so hastily
summarized, we shall probably never understand either
how Epicurus conceived the material being of his Gods
or what Cicero meant in § 49. That passage, as it stands,
is a slough in which ingenious explanations without
number have merely been swallowed up.

Epicureanism has indeed its pitfalls for the historian
of philosophy, as Guyau's remarkable interpretation of the
doctrine of Atomic Declination shows. Guyau's exposition of ' Spontaneity in Things ' has a certain philosophical value, but the theory of the Epicurean Gods
which we have been examining carries no such interest.

It is not only without evidence, but it conflicts with Epicurus's most cherished doctrines. Epicurus would have shuddered to see the foundation-stone of his theology thus moved from its place.[1] The theory of Scott and Giussani neither grows organically out of Epicurean doctrine, nor does it bring Epicurus's theology any more than before into touch with the actual facts of the world or of human nature. These Deities-in-flux are merely the figment of a scholar's brain. It is only as a fanciful distortion of Epicurus's actual teaching that this theory falls to be mentioned in the history of that strange, and, indeed, sad ' Comedy ' of the Epicurean Gods.

[1] See Chapter XII., pp. 279, 280.

APPENDIX XII

THE ANOMALY OF FREE-WILL IN A HEDONISTIC SYSTEM

Chapter XV., p. 331.

GUYAU has pointed out with much force the anomaly of Free-will in a system which makes Pleasure the chief end. He says :

' In the problem of Free-will we find the ancient and the modern Epicureans in entire disagreement with each other. We know that Epicurus admits Free-will, and places not only in man, but also in Nature and the atoms, a spontaneity which derives from itself its principle of action. On the contrary, Hobbes, Helvétius, d'Holbach —in a word, all the modern Epicureans without exception—reject Free-will, and show themselves frankly determinist, sometimes, even, like Hobbes and La Mettrie, extreme fatalists. We have not here to examine the absolute truth of these opposite doctrines, but we may ask ourselves which is the most in conformity with Epicurean principles. Then we have to admit that the belief in Free-will is an anomaly in the system of Epicurus. He, after having laid down happiness as the chief end, recognizes that tranquillity of soul is the necessary condition of this happiness, and he believes that the condition of a universal necessity dominating Nature would be incompatible with tranquillity of soul. According to him, we know there is something gloomy and disturbing in the notion of fatalism : it is on this account that he rejects it. Then, once that he has begun to reject it, with a remarkable spirit of logic he rejects it all round, and places spontaneity in everything. What

he has not proved is that this spontaneity could exist at
all : he does not even make the attempt to prove it.   For
him moral liberty is a manifest fact of consciousness.
Then, having laid down the Free-will of man, he deduces
from it with much force the spontaneity of Nature ; but
he does not perceive that of two things one or the other
holds, either moral liberty is uncertain, and then his
system is wrapped in the same uncertainty, or else it is
certain, and then it is a new principle with which one has
to reckon.   If I have liberty, I can found ethics upon it,
and can entirely dispense with the principle of self-interest.
Duty can be deduced from the idea of liberty without any
need to appeal to pleasure.   That a determinist should
be a utilitarian is easily understood ; but that a partisan
of Free-will, who believes he feels within him something absolute ("je ne sais quoi d'absolu"), a cause living and acting
of itself, possessing an intrinsic value and dignity—that
he should go and submit it to an outside rule of action,
divert it toward a foreign end, and make of it an instrument of pleasure—here is a *thorough* inconsistency which
the modern Epicureans have been right to eschew.   As
to this point, the Epicurean system has acquired in our
own day a new strength and homogeneity.   Epicurus
complained that the idea of universal determinism weighs
on the human soul, for it is a pain for man to sacrifice to
Nature his full and entire independence.   He forgot that
ethics, no more than any other science, can enter into this
question of individual preferences.   Every science seeks
not after that which pleases the intelligence or the feelings,
but after that which is.   It pursues not absolute happiness, that Utopia of ancient Epicureanism, but the relative happiness which is compatible with realities, and it
does not recoil before any truth, however stern it may
be.'[1]

[1] 'La Morale d'Épicure,' pp. 284, 285.

APPENDIX XIII

THE CONCEPTION OF PLEASURE AS THE CHIEF END IN
THE CYRENAICS AND IN EPICURUS

Chapter XV., p. 333.

BORN in the wealthy and luxurious Greek colony of
Cyrene, Aristippus went to Athens and became a pupil
of Socrates, by whom he was profoundly influenced. But
he always retained a large portion of independence, and
soon he diverged greatly from the Socratic spirit and
teaching. Not improbably he had brought with him from
his native city habits of luxury and extravagance. He
was always a man of the world, as well as a philosopher.

Socrates placed the highest happiness in virtue, which
he identified with true knowledge. Aristippus identified
' the Good,' which Socrates was ever inquiring into with
what is agreeable, with pleasure. Pleasure and pain he
regarded as the only criteria of good and evil. All feeling
consists in emotion of soul or sensation of body, so he
identified pleasure and pain of either with motion :
pleasure is ' gentle motion,' pain is ' violent motion.'
He held that ' temperance ' or ' self-control,' the main
Socratic virtue, alone renders us capable of enjoyment.
Now, as the feeling of the body is, on the whole, far more
intense than the feeling of the mind, he held that pleasure
of the body produces a far livelier and stronger sensation
of the gentle order than pleasure of the mind ; therefore
Aristippus inferred that pleasures of the body are better
than intellectual pleasures. The chief aim of life, then, is
to secure a series of pleasurable sensations. Further, he
specially identified pleasure with the gratification of the

moment. Herein lay Aristippus's distinctive doctrine. He expressly refused to consider the happiness of the whole life as the chief good. This, for him, is the pleasure of the moment. Past pleasures have ceased to be ; future pleasures are uncertain. Therefore, his rule of life was to cultivate the art of enjoying the present moment.

' The Cyrenaics think,' says Diogenes, ' that there is a distinction between the chief good and a life of happiness ; for the chief good is a particular pleasure, but happiness is a state consisting of a number of particular pleasures, in which are included both those which are past and those which are future. And they consider that the particular pleasure is desirable for its own sake, but that happiness is desirable not for its own sake, but for that of the particular pleasures.'[1]

As to any distinction between various pleasures, he held there is none, except in their intensity. Pleasure is a good from whatever source it may derive, even from the most unbecoming ones.[2] Here his Naturalism is prominent.

Since none but the wise man possesses self-control, it is he alone who can be really happy. Aristippus asserted most strongly that a man must not be a slave to pleasure. If any given pleasure is bound presently to produce a greater pain, we must avoid it. Therefore, the thing most essential to the enjoyment of life is prudence. If we are slaves to appetite on the one hand, or to superstition on the other, we cannot get the good of life ; hence he insists on the study of philosophy. ' It is better to be a beggar,' he said, ' than to be an ignorant person ; for the beggar lacks money only, but the ignorant man lacks humanity.'[3] Without culture we cannot be truly human ; the ignorant man sitting on the marble bench of the theatre is ' like a stone sitting upon a stone.'[4] Compared with the mere rich man, the philosopher is like the

---

[1] Diog. L., ii. 87, 88.   [2] *Ibid.*, ii., 88.
[3] οἱ μὲν γὰρ χρημάτων, οἱ δὲ ἀνθρωπισμοῦ δέονται (Diog. L., ii. 70).   [4] *Ibid.*, ii. 72.

physician compared with the man who is sick. Philosophy, therefore, is essential to happiness. As a rule, it is the wise man who is happy.[1]

The Cyrenaic ' wise man,' then, is a well-informed, educated, shrewd man of the world, not wanting in good-nature, a delightful companion, who, while ever seeking enjoyment unscrupulously and even in base ways, is yet determined that he will remain the master of his appetites. This, however, Aristippus owes to Socrates. His own doctrines would never secure it. The true master of pleasure, he declared, is not the man who abstains from it entirely, but the man who can use and not abuse it. This is both the harder and the better course.[2] Here Aristippus is undoubtedly in the right.

It is impossible to look on Aristippus without some respect. As emphasizing in his own peculiar way the necessity of self-command, Aristippus is truly a disciple of Socrates. No doubt he also admired Socrates's independent attitude as to public opinion, and in his own strange fashion he imitated it. Moreover, he is no vulgar pleasure-seeker. He appears to have been genuinely repelled by debauchery and excess. He can smile at adverse fortune, and remains master of himself, relying on his inward resources. When Plato said to him, ' To you alone it is given to wear becomingly both the rich mantle and the ragged cloak,' he spoke, no doubt, with genuine admiration. We have to condemn Aristippus as a philosophical sensualist, but his teaching is not, perhaps, more dangerous practically than the extreme opposite type, as represented, for example, by the morose, narrow, and self-satisfied type of religion which in the England of the early nineteenth century too often disgraced the great name of Puritanism. To deny that human nature is meant to blossom in its due season into the flower of

---

[1] Diog. L., x. 91.

[2] τὸ κρατεῖν καὶ μὴ ἡττᾶσθαι ἡδόνων κράτιστον, οὐ τὸ μὴ χρῆσθαι (Diog. L., ii. 75). κρατεῖ ἡδόνης οὐχ ὁ ἀπεχόμενος ἀλλ' ὁ χρωμένος μὲν, μὴ παρεκφερόμενος δὲ (Stob., ' Flor.,' xvii. 18).

gladness is to deny an essential attribute of the Good.[1] It is as deep an atheism as to be ever seeking to force Pleasure into a perennial and artificial bloom, as did the Cyrenaics.

Aristippus aims at cheerfulness in all circumstances. He seeks pleasure, but can do without it. Riches for themselves he sets no value on, but lavishes them when he has them. He asserts himself to esteem above all things ' freedom,' and does so with some truth. In a notable conversation reported by Xenophon he claims to have discovered for himself a ' middle path ' by which he is to attain freedom. This is to belong to no one State, but to roam the world, and so to escape the duties alike of subject and ruler—a course of which Socrates points out the difficulties.[2] (In this respect his attitude is as unpatriotic as that of Epicurus.) Aristippus was once asked what spectacle in the world he regarded as a marvellous one. He replied : ' That of a just[3] and temperate

[1] The books of ' Mark Rutherford ' will show what is meant. It ought to be needless to explain (though this writer seems to forget it) that the form of religion which he so subtly analyzes, merciless yet admiring, is but a one-sided and bastard Puritanism. The overpowering strain of the struggle against tyranny may excuse some over-seriousness in the Puritan, but he was no unmanly pietist, denying the claims of the body, and withdrawing from the pursuits and pastimes of other men from fear of temptation. These are the faults of safer times and a feebler race. In this how unlike Milton ! ' He that can apprehend and consider vice, with all her baits and seeming pleasures, and yet abstain, and yet distinguish, and yet prefer that which is truly better, he is the true warfaring Christian. I cannot praise a fugitive and cloistered virtue, unexercised and unbreathed, that never sallies out and sees her adversary, but slinks out of the race where that immortal garland is to be run for not without dust and heat. Assuredly we bring not innocence into the world ; we bring impurity much rather. That which purifies us is trial, and trial is by what is contrary ' (' Areopagitica ').

[2] Xen., ' Mem.,' ii. 1, 8.

[3] ἐπιεικής, this meaning a man who gives others more than their due, who is ' equitable ' rather than ' just.' See the noted definition of the term in Aristot., ' Rhetoric,' i. 13. The word has the general meaning of ' good.' The anecdote is from Stob., ' Flor.,' xxxvii. 25.

man, who, though living in the midst of the vicious, is
not diverted from his course.' However perverse the
attitude, there is something brave and strenuous here.
The tranquillity which Epicurus sought by living out of
the world is contemptible compared with Aristippus's
pride of conscious self-restraint, rejoicing to prove itself
adequate to all experiences in life, and shunning none.
Whatever adventure or ambition challenges him, he is
resolved not to miss it, even though scruples have to be
laid aside. For him, in the sense of any essential difference, there is no Parting of the Ways. Surely a difficult
ideal, and one pregnant in strange and unseemly situa-
tions ! No wonder that Socrates considered Aristippus's
' middle way ' impracticable.

But though admiring certain features of his character,
in others Aristippus repels us. The ancient world classes
him among the followers of Socrates, and Aristippus
regarded himself as such. He spoke of Socrates with
gratitude and devotion. If anything good could be
spoken of himself by others, he said, it was owing to
Socrates.[1] But he failed in his attempt to combine
Socratic doctrines with the pursuit of Pleasure. Let him
extol philosophy as he will, it remains true that neither
philosophy nor religion any more than friendship will
endure to be traded in as a means to another end. Aristippus held all actions to be in themselves morally indifferent : for us, their results are all that matter. He
held, as we shall see, that it is possible—thanks to philosophy—to live for the pleasures of the moment, and yet
retain perfect freedom of soul. But the two aims cannot
be reconciled. True ' freedom ' of spirit is only for him
who is independent of present circumstances which may
be painful, and who can, when necessary, live in the past
and future. With all his shrewd wisdom, with all his
keen appreciation of knowledge and culture, he lacks
true dignity and self-respect. He calls himself the ' comrade of Socrates '; he is highly gifted, and feels the dignity

[1] Diog. L., ii. 71.

158 APPENDIX XIII

of intellectual life, yet he can submit to gross insults from
his patron Dionysius. Socrates, who read his character
with profound insight, while evidently respecting his
talent,[1] warns him most emphatically as one who has lost
his path, and enforces his warning with the immortal
picture of the ' Choice of Hercules.'[2] When Plato, in the
' Phædo,' enumerates the friends who gathered round
Socrates on that last day in the prison, one of the speakers
asks, ' Was Aristippus there ?' And Phædo answers that
he was absent, and was said to be in Ægina. His presence
in the prison could have exposed him to little danger.
Probably he absented himself in order to escape a painful
and harrowing experience, and his philosophy would
justify him here.

As to Aristippus's conception of knowledge, which
closely resembled that of Protagoras, and its relation to
his ethics, I may refer to Zeller's admirable section.[3]
Aristippus is, in fact, more in touch with the Sophistic
movement, both in its dialectic and in its tainted ethics,
than with Socrates. But we have specially to do with
his doctrine of Pleasure.

According to Epicurus, every pleasure, whatever it be,
is good in itself,[4] his exclusion of any moral element from
' the Good ' being the main principle of utilitarianism.
From this standpoint the past antecedents of the pleasure,
whether these be degrading or not, count for nothing.
Omitting, then, the consideration of the past, what of the
future ? Here a new problem faces us : What if the
result of a present pleasure be future pain ? It is here
that Epicurus diverges largely from the Cyrenaics. Aris-

[1] Some of the most important discussions in the ' Memorabilia ' are held with Aristippus—e.g., that on the relation between
the Good and the Beautiful (book iii. 18).
[2] Xen., ' Mem.,' ii. 1. Socrates refers this fable to Prodicus,
who seems to have used it as a subject for oratorical display (see
§ 34).
[3] ' Socrates,' English Translation, pp. 348-353, and notes.
[4] πᾶσα οὖν ἡδονὴ διὰ τὸ φύσιν ἔχειν οἰκείαν ἀγαθόν (Diog. L.,
x. 129). οὐδεμία ἡδονὴ καθ' ἑαυτὸ κακὸν (x. 141).

tippus distinguishes between ' happiness ' as affecting our whole life, including pleasures, both past and future, and the ' chief good,' which is the particular pleasure of the moment.[1]   The foresight and prudence which subordinate our actions to a higher end seem to him a kind of slavery. But he forgot that, in wishing to make himself independent of the future, he made himself a slave to the present, with one pleasure competing against another in its proffers of gratification.   This is to deprive ourselves of all freedom of action.   Our reason will not allow us to sever any act from the past which has produced, or the future which may issue from it.   To do this is to exist in a fool's paradise.

Epicurus's doctrine of pleasure is in its basis the same as that of Aristippus, but he has modified it profoundly by introducing into it the idea of the future.   Guyau says :

' Epicurus finds a very simple means of establishing a distinction between different pleasures.   Instead of taking them in themselves, consider them in relation to their consequences, in their relation to the whole of life.   It is evident that there are many pleasures followed by pain, sometimes by a pain greater than the pleasure.   These pleasures we pass by, and let alone in order to seek beyond them for pleasures which are less dangerous. For the wise man imposes on himself before all else the law of being consistent with himself, of extending his thought far enough into the future to prevent it from contradicting itself, of governing his desires sufficiently to hinder them from turning against themselves. . . .   In the teaching of Aristippus, then, pleasures, variable and manifold, carried the soul away at random ;

---

[1] ' The Cyrenaics think that there is a distinction between the chief Good and happiness, for the chief Good, they hold, is a particular pleasure, but happiness is a state, consisting of a number of particular pleasures, including both those which are past and those which are to come.   And they hold that each particular pleasure is desirable for its own sake, but that happiness is desirable not for its own sake, but for the particular pleasures ' (Diog. L., ii. 87, 88).

but in the system of Epicurus we see them arrange themselves in view of an end, which is nothing else than themselves, but themselves stripped of every foreign and inferior element. Already in point of logic there is evident progress. Thought does not exhaust itself in every particular pleasure ; the will does not parcel itself out and divide itself between various pleasures, and, athwart time, we catch glimpses of a unity which we may pursue, and in which we may hope.

' This moment in which Epicurus and Aristippus commence to differ in opinion and to diverge the one from the other deserves our attention, for this is the moment when a doctrine which is to play a more and more striking part in the history of moral philosophy takes its birth and first manifests itself. As soon as pleasure, instead of being considered as an immediate end, is fertilized by the idea of time, and becomes a truly highest and final end, set before us as the aim and goal of the whole life, it takes a new name, and the doctrine of *Pleasure* is changed into the doctrine of *Utility*.'[1]

Herein the Epicurean ethics outstrips that of Aristippus : it places before our eyes, if not an ideal, yet a whole. Aristippus sought to do away with the tendency to look beyond each particular pleasure ; but the utilitarianism of Epicurus gives us a certain degree of freedom in the face of a present pleasure or pain. We may annihilate these by the idea of a superior pleasure. Restrained to the immediate moment, each of these threatens to master us, but we dominate it when we view it in relation to the whole of life. To the instincts and passions of the soul, says Guyau, time is what space is to the atoms of Epicurus : they find room, they arrange and calm themselves, and do not jostle each other. ' Is there not an æsthetic pleasure,' he asks, ' in this reasoned arrangement of life, subordinating the parts to the whole—in this happiness, which substitutes itself for pleasures, and while completing them thereby purifies them ? Life

[1] ' La Morale d'Épicure,' 1881, pp. 39, 40.

thus becomes a sort of frame with its margins undeter-
mined, on which the wise man, this " artist of happiness,"
groups his emotions—places some in the first rank, the
others in the second; brings the former to the front;
thrusts the others into the background, and lets them
drop into oblivion. *He contemplates and admires this
work, at once so beautiful and so rational. . . .'*[1]

We need not follow Guyau further, nor comment on
these words written by a youth of nineteen, of feeble
physique, brilliant gifts, and high enthusiasms. The
' instincts and passions,' whether it be ambition or the
lower appetites that dominate, are not so easily silenced
and ' dropped into oblivion.' If it is only by adding up
consequences on either side, and carefully balancing the
safer pleasures against the more dangerous, the longer
against the momentary; if it is only thus that the plan
of our lives is to be made a beautiful picture, most men,
at the close of the day, are likely to find a blurred and
unsightly canvas confronting them.

It is plain that Epicurus, even more than Aristippus,
attributes the utmost importance to intelligence ($\phi\rho\prime\nu\eta\sigma\iota\varsigma$).
It remains only a means, but an indispensable one. It
not merely directs all our actions towards pleasure; it
must also organize pleasures and even pains, in view of
the supreme pleasure. ' Every pleasure, therefore,' says
Epicurus, ' is good on account of its own nature, but not
every pleasure ought to be chosen, just as every pain is
evil, and yet every pain must not be avoided. But it is
right to estimate all these things by the comparison
($\sigma\upsilon\mu\mu\acute{\epsilon}\tau\rho\eta\sigma\iota\varsigma$) and view of what is suitable and what is
unsuitable. . . . We think many pains better than
pleasures when, if we endure the pain even for a long
time, a greater pleasure follows.'[2]

A recent writer, Walter Pater, has given to his philosophy of life the title of ' The New Cyrenæicism.'[3]   Accord-

---

[1] 'La Morale d'Épicure,' 1881, p. 43.
[2] Diog. L., x. 129, 130.
[3] A chapter of ' Marius the Epicurean,' vol. i., is thus headed.

ing to this the end of life is through our sense of beauty
to obtain the greatest number and the highest kind of
agreeable or exquisite sensations from the beauty of the
world in earth and sky, or in the human form, and in all
our experience to be alive to this as well as to be in touch
with all recorded instances of human life which exhibit
' the heroic, the impassioned, the ideal,' by which in their
turn our emotions are stimulated, and we receive other
impressions.   For such a man as Pater there might be no
temptation to grossness in such an ideal of life, in the
study ' how such actual moments as they passed might
be made to yield their utmost by the most dexterous
training of capacity.'[1]   Rather to him the sense of
beauty was a kind of worship.   And yet, unless the
ethical dominates this constant sensuous receptivity, life
tends to become a slavery to æsthetic impressions, and, in
youth especially, the soul is in utmost danger of being
drugged and the will weakened till a moral apathy results,
and we take no side in the battle between good and evil.

One asks, What would Aristippus have said of this
modern disciple ?   Probably that Pater's whole attitude
to life is that of a highly appreciative spectator, watching
the banqueters, enjoying with fine discrimination the
savour of the viands, the colour and bouquet of the wines,
yet never joining in the feast.   ' I at least,' Aristippus
might have said, ' am not afraid to live.'   In this dreaming
æsthetic, *passive* attitude to life Pater comes far nearer to
Epicurus than to Aristippus.   If Plato be right in defining
the chief good as ' living well,' by this meaning the full
exercise of our faculties in action,[2] surely in so far
Aristippus, with his wide, if somewhat soiled, experience,
came nearer the mark than did Pater.   If Pater's ideal
was one long dreaming of poetry, Aristippus in his adven-
turous career was surely *living* poetry *of a kind*.   In actual
life men do not need to seek for sensations ; they come,
and, it may be, come overwhelmingly.

[1] Marius, vol. i., p. 146.
[2] See 'Lucretius,' vol. i., p. 337.

APPENDIX XIV

Chapter XV., p. 334.

Guyau has treated with his usual acuteness the points of
development in the doctrine of Pleasure in the various
successors of Epicurus. No system can be judged, he
says, till it has completed its development, and we cannot
correctly appreciate Epicureanism apart from the doctrines of the English school.

He says : ' All Epicureans (and this is the fundamental
idea of their doctrine) agree in affirming that pleasure
or pain are the sole forces which actuate men, the sole
levers by aid of which we can produce an action of whatsoever kind.

' This principle being laid down, Epicurus and his
successors conclude from it that, pleasure being the sole
end of man, morality ought to consist for every individual
in the art of procuring for himself the greatest sum of
personal pleasures. Morality thus understood is nothing
else, as a utilitarian has himself said, than the reducing
of selfishness to rule. Hobbes attempted before Spinoza
to construct a " geometry of morals," Helvetius constructed a " physics of morals," d'Holbach a " physiology of morals " ; but, under these diverse names, Epicurean morality is, in short, never anything more than the
quest of personal advantage : it rests upon the audacious
confusion of actuality and duty. In *actuality*, it believes

the individual pursues only his own pleasure. In point
of *right*, too, it is his own pleasure that he ought to pursue,
whether this pleasure happen to be in opposition to that
of others or happen to be in harmony with it. Nevertheless, all Epicureans, including even La Mettrie, agree
in recommending the individual not to confine himself
within a foolish selfishness, but to cultivate friendship,
to show himself sociable and benevolent. According to
them, there is in most cases a harmony between the
pleasure of the individual and that of others; but let it
be clearly understood this is no fundamental and primal
harmony. The selfishnesses keep time together like clocks,
without mixing or forming any profound union; and
morality itself does not aim at producing this union,
because it would be impossible. On this point, again,
Epicureanism has made very little advance in France.
D'Alembert, d'Holbach, and Volney occasionally an-
ticipate our contemporary English school, but they
make haste always to return from it to personal
advantage as the sincere principle of all morals. Here,
then, there is a notable divergence between the Epicureans
and the present English school. This divergence in-
creases more and more as we advance from Bentham to
Stuart Mill and, above all, to Mr. Spencer, from whose
principles we can for the first time construct an almost
complete physics or physiology of morals. The English
moralists always retain personal pleasure as the sole lever
capable of setting men in motion ; only, instead of laying
down this pleasure itself as the end of a moral being,
they labour with all their strength to make him pursue
the pleasure of others. Expressed under this form, their
utilitarianism seems at first manifestly inconsistent, and
we shall inquire elsewhere if it does not really contain
some inconsistency. Still, there is something profound
in this doctrine to which I must now call attention.

' In a word, what would a purely personal and selfish
pleasure be ? Are there any pleasures of this sort, and
what part do they play in life ? When one descends the

...erapy

adiological physics

he three faces of Eve

sychoanalytic treatment of schizophrenia and
        characteriological disorders

he Use of LSD in psychotherapy and alcoholism

e development of modern surgery

e management of intelligence

w to sell fashion; what retailers should know
        about women's wear

shion design for moderns

USIC

eating art from anything

eing and knowing

rms and substances in the art...

187
M388 1

Mason John
Auentin

187
Oct 8

Epsuer

Mobregen

scale of beings, we see that the sphere in which each moves is narrow and almost shut in.   On the other hand, when we ascend to a higher order of creatures, we see their sphere of action opening, extending, blending more and more with the activities of others. The " Myself " becomes less and less separated from other " Selves," or rather we have more and more need of them to establish our own position and to live our own lives. Now the same scale of progress which thought traverses has already in some degree been worked out for humankind by evolution.   According to Mr. Spencer, its starting-point has been selfishness, but selfishness and the necessities of life of themselves draw human beings together ; feelings corresponding to this tendency have come to birth little by little, and have, as it were, hidden the selfish feelings from which they are derived. Thus what Mr. Spencer calls the " ego-altruistic sentiments " come into existence, and we are progressing towards a point at which selfishness, receding more and more into the background, becoming less and less recognizable as selfishness, will yield place almost altogether to " altruistic " feelings.[1] When this ideal point is reached, man will no longer, so to say, be able to enjoy in solitary fashion ; his pleasure will be, as it were, a concert, into which the pleasure of others will enter by right of being a necessary constituent ; and even now, for the most part, is not this the case ?   If we compare the part played by " altruism " in ordinary life with that left to pure selfishness, we shall see how much greater relatively is that of the former ; even pleasures such as eating and drinking, which, since they are entirely of the body, are the most egoistic, only attain their full charm when we share them with others. That the social feelings hold the predominance ought to be recognized in all theories and in whatever fashion we may conceive of morals. The fact is that no dogma can shut up the human heart. We cannot maim ourselves, and

[1] These words, I need hardly say, were written in the enthusiasm of Guyau's youth.

pure selfishness would be nonsense and an impossibility. Just as, according to the English school, the " Myself " is, in point of fact, an illusion, as there is no personality, as we are made up of an infinitude of beings (*êtres*) and small consciousnesses, so we may say egoistic pleasure is an illusion. My personal pleasure does not exist without the pleasure of others ; the whole of society must collaborate in it more or less, from the little society which surrounds me, from my family, on to the great society in which I live. It cannot be otherwise ; that would be contrary to my *interests*. My pleasure, in order to lose nothing of its intensity, must preserve the whole of its extension. In a word, the ethics of the English school, which we may consider as the development of Epicureanism, form also the best criticism of it ; they demonstrate the insufficiency of the principle of pure selfishness, an insufficiency which is already manifest in Epicurus and the Roman Epicureans.'[1]

As yet the world has not reached the stage when the social sentiments can drive out selfishness. Reason might prove to the average man that selfish indulgence is ' against his interests,' but the human passions must hear a stronger voice before they will obey.

[1] ' La Morale d'Épicure,' pp. 281-283.

APPENDIX XV

EPICURUS defines Pleasure, which he assumed as the
Chief End, as being a state of repose of body and soul.
He deduces from this that the ideal of every being must
be to seek peace and calm within itself, and apart from
any outside influence. This doctrine at first sight has an
air of nobleness, but in practice its consequences are
disastrous, as we have seen. Guyau makes the following
criticism, from his own point of view a characteristic one.
Hobbes, he says, made a happy change on Epicureanism,
by returning to the notion of Aristippus that Pleasure is
in its essence movement, action, energy, and therefore
progress. ' Unquestionably one may maintain with
Epicurus that Pleasure is accompanied by an inward
equilibrium, a harmony of all our faculties ; but this is,
in short, only the condition of Pleasure, and if we examine it more profoundly we shall recognize that this
inward equilibrium does precisely allow to us a more and
more expansive action in all directions. In our own days
the English school will go still further : it will show that
our activity in its progressive development is accompanied by the capacity of feeling (*sensibilité*). Pleasure
is not a changeless thing, as Epicurus believed ; it varies
constantly. Habit and heredity attach it to new actions.
It thus submits to the great law of universal evolution; it
is in itself the evolution and development of the creature.'[1]

[1] ' La Morale d'Épicure,' p. 284.

APPENDIX XVI

LUCRETIUS'S ASSERTION OF LAW IN NATURE

I. *Lucretius's reasoning in* ii. 251-293 *has been generally misunderstood. Does he conceive the Laws of Nature as opposed to the ' fœdera fati'?—Mr. Benn's assertion that Lucretius grasps the fact of Law in Nature only from its negative side.*

IT is not easy to grasp Lucretius's reasoning throughout this paragraph, and not a few writers appear to have misunderstood it. In his admirable chapter on ' The Philosophy of Lucretius,' Professor Sellar observes that, according to Lucretius, creation is the result not of any Divine working, ' but of certain processes extending through infinite time, by means of which the atoms have at length been able to combine and work together in accordance with their ultimate conditions. The conception of these ultimate conditions and of their relations to one another involves some more vital agency than that of blind chance or an iron fatalism (ii. 254). The *fœdera naturai* are opposed to the *fœdera fati*. The idea of law in Nature, as understood by Lucretius, is not merely that of invariable sequence or concomitance of phenomena. It implies at least the further idea of a *secreta facultas*[1]

---

[1] At p. 319, Professor Sellar says : ' A secret faculty in the atoms, distinct from their other properties, is assumed. Thus he says :

' At primordia gignundis in rebus oportet
Naturam clandestinam cœcamque adhibere.'

i. 778, 779.

in the original elements' (p. 335). The most careful
study of all the doctrines of Lucretius's system and their
bearing on each other shows us no ground for admitting
any opposition between *fœdera fati* and *fœdera naturai*.
Lucretius, it is true, does not believe in Fate, so far as
men are concerned. In the moral world he asserts that
there is no such thing. At the same time, 'Fate,' or
'Necessity,' is a name occasionally given, as we have
seen,[1] both by Epicurus and Lucretius, to the order of
Nature resulting from natural laws. The *fœdera fati* (a
mere synonym for *fatum*) and the *fœdera naturai* are never
really opposed to each other by Lucretius. Such a conception is altogether foreign to him.

Again, Mr. Alfred Benn, in an able article on 'Epicurus
and Lucretius' in the *Westminster Review* (April, 1882),
insists repeatedly that Epicurus has no title to the credit
of asserting the reign of Law. He says that the Stoics
have more claim to this honour, and in their physics
'came nearer than Lucretius to the standpoint of modern
science,' and even asserts that 'Epicurus expressly refused
to accept such a doctrine' (the universality of law in

This quotation is translated as follows in the note : 'But it is
necessary that the atoms, in the act of creation, should exercise
some secret, invisible faculty.' Putting aside the fact that
secreta facultas (a phrase occurring only once in the poem, at
i. 173) cannot possibly mean a 'secret faculty,' and that i. 778-779
means, as Mr. Munro has shown, merely that the atoms must not
possess any secondary qualities, such as colour, the expressions
used by Professor Sellar are not consistent with Lucretius's
system. His atoms possess no properties apart from those which
he assigns them—figure, perfect hardness, etc., and also Free-
will. How, then, can we find room within the rigid four walls of
Epicureanism for anything like a 'vital agency,' either as working
in Nature or as finding expression in the laws of Nature ? Instead of this, how often does Lucretius tell us that the origin and
the maintenance of the world and its life is due to a mere coincidence among the atoms !

[1] See p. 75, notes 1 and 2, where all the references to *fatum*
are collated. *Cf.* especially v. 309, 310, where *fati finis*, 'the
limits of fate,' evidently refers to the same thing as *naturæ
fœdera*.

Nature). Mr. Benn brings little evidence to support this remarkable statement. Probably it is based in part on a misconception of Epicurus's doctrine of Atomic Declination. Referring to the latter, he says : ' Apparently neither Epicurus nor his disciples saw that in discarding the invariable sequence of phenomena they annulled to the same extent the possibility of human foresight and the adaptation of means to ends' (p. 323). The writer, possibly under the influence of M. Guyau, assumes that the consequence of Free-will existing in the atoms must be a power of spontaneous movement in all material substances, which must interfere with the regular order of Nature. But, as we saw, Epicurus held that Free-will, though active in the atoms, is nullified when these combine in matter. Thus, it did not, according to Epicurus's conception of it, at all interfere with Law. Again, he says : ' Lucretius expressly tells us (ii. 255, " ex infinito ne causam causa sequatur ") that the law of causation is broken through by the clinamen.' The writer here fails to see that Lucretius draws a sharp distinction between the world of Nature, subject to law, and the human mind, which is free. So far as Nature—that is, the method of the world's ongoings—is concerned, without taking into account the agency of man, Lucretius holds that *causum causa sequitur*—' cause *does* follow cause.' The truth is that Lucretius had the firmest grasp of the fact of Law. At the same time he holds that the mind of man is not subject to the *fœdera naturæ*. Free-will is a *libera potestas*. But perhaps Mr. Benn holds that a belief in Free-will is not consistent with a belief in Laws of Nature. This would help us to understand his assertion that Epicurus did not to any extent believe in Law. Again, he says (p. 333) that ' when Lucretius speaks of *fœdera naturæ*, he means not what we understand by Laws of Nature . . . but rather the limiting possibilities of existence.' In fact, Mr. Benn holds that Lucretius grasped merely the negative side of natural order. A less fair criticism than this could hardly be made. The *majestas cognita rerum* which so inspired Lucretius was something more than ' negative ' knowledge.

In connection with this subject, attention may be called to a strange misconception of Grote's regarding a far greater thinker than Epicurus. Socrates, he asserts, believed that Laws of Nature are not discoverable by man.

II. *Grote on Socrates. Attitude of Socrates to Physical Science.*

After pointing out that in all ordinary pursuits success depends largely upon human industry and diligence in learning all that can be learned, Xenophon (' Mem.,' i. 8) says : ' " The gods," Socrates said, " reserve for their own knowledge the most important particulars [*i.e.*, the results] concerned in such arts, of which particulars not one is manifest to men ; for neither is he who has sown his field well certain who shall reap the fruit of it, nor is he who has built a house well certain who shall live in it, nor yet he who is skilled in generalship certain whether it is for his advantage to act as general," ' and so on with many other instances.

Grote (vol. viii., p. 226) comments thus on the passage : ' With reference to matters of human practice, Socrates held that the gods " manage all the current phenomena upon principles of constant and intelligible sequence, so that everyone who chose might learn. . . . Even in these, however, the gods did not condescend to submit *all* the phenomena to constant antecedence and consequence, but reserve to themselves the capital turns and junctures for special sentence." ' After this somewhat clumsy paraphrase of Xenophon's words above quoted, Grote goes on to say that this attempt of Socrates to draw the line between what was and what was not scientifically discoverable proves ' Socrates's conviction that the scientific and the religious point of view mutually excluded one another, so that, where the latter began, the former ended.' Elsewhere (p. 295) he draws the following inference from the same passage : ' About physics Socrates was more than a sceptic. He thought that man could know nothing. The gods did not intend that man should acquire any such information, and therefore managed matters in such a way as to be beyond his ken for all except the simplest phenomena of daily wants.'

It is strange that so utter a misinterpretation of these words of Xenophon should come from so acute a thinker as Grote. All that Xenophon says is : ' Socrates held that the *results* and *success* of human effort are not scientifically and infallibly discoverable. The gods do not intend certainty *of this kind* for man. Thus, the farmer may with utmost toil and skill plough, sow, and tend the crop, but as regards profit to himself in vain. Between him and the harvest any one of the infinite forms of what we call " accident " may step in. Thus, the enemy may reap his fields.'

Moreover, Socrates did not believe in occasional Divine interferences with natural laws. He held that the knowledge and care of the Deity are continual and coextensive with the whole material world and with every human act (' Mem.,' I., iv. 17, 18).

Socrates did, indeed, discourage the study of physical science, chiefly for the reason that the ' science ' of his day was mainly guess-work, and was not based on experiment. But he was no agnostic as to Law in Nature.

PART III

NOTES AND COMMENTS UPON THE FORMER VOLUME

By PROFESSOR J. S. REID

NOTES AND COMMENTS UPON THE FORMER VOLUME

By PROFESSOR J. S. REID

I AM indebted for the following criticisms, containing many valuable and fresh suggestions, to Professor J. S. Reid.   One or two other criticisms, with comments of my own, are included.   I have brought together first the notes referring to the history of Lucretius's time.

' *Page* 3.—In Cicero's " Fam.," x. 33, written after the Battle of Mutina, the reference is not to the uninhabited condition of Italy, but partly to the loss of life up to that date, and partly to the future effect on the country of the bloodshed in the civil war.   The other passage does imply that these are desolate tracts in Italy, as, indeed, was the case in the time of Tiberius Gracchus.   Is not *vacuum Tibur* rather " leisurely Tibur " than desolate ?   See the context, and *cf. vacuæ Athenæ*, Ep. II., ii. 81.'

[The instances quoted by me are unfortunate.   Mommsen says : ' The population of Italy was visibly on the decline.   Especially was this true of the pastoral districts, such as Apulia . . . and of the region around Rome, where the Campagna was annually becoming more desolate under the constant reciprocal action of the retrograde agriculture and the increasing malaria. . . .   In Latium, in particular, the stock of men capable of bearing arms had totally vanished ' (' History of Rome,' English translation, vol. v., 1894, pp. 394, 395).—J. M.]

' *Page* 4.—" Limited franchise " is a little misleading. The franchise was intended to be full, but, owing to the civil war immediately succeeding, the necessary readjustments of the tribe-territories and the registration of the new citizens was not carried out till 70 B.C.

'*Page* 5.—Sallust's moralizings (by an immoral man) are conventional rhetoric, and not worth much as evidence. I am myself inclined to regard Sallust's report of the debate in the Senate as highly imaginative in its details. Probably only the main proposals are authentic.

'*Page* 7.—Gwatkin's statement is vastly exaggerated. The moral and religious element underlying the ceremonial forms is very generally underestimated.

'*Page* 7.—Prolonged study of Cæsar's life has led me to form a very different estimate of it from that of Froude and Mommsen. The latter was, of course, master of the material; but Mommsen loved the " mailed fist " for its own sake, and this warped his judgment.

'*Page* 9.—I think Roman want of organization rather than corruption was the cause of the success of the pirates. From the dawn of history down to 1816, when the English fleet blew up that of the Algerian pirates, the Mediterranean has only been free from piracy for about two centuries and a half, from the time that Augustus established the three fleets till about the end of the Severi.

'*Page* 12.—The facts about *novitas* are quite as striking earlier, in the period between the Second Punic War and that of Marius. But I think you ought to strike out the words " or prætor." A good many *novi homines* got as far as the prætorship. The consulship was the barrier. The condition of the *publicus ager* is very hard to determine, owing to the lack of evidence; but it is not likely that any " vast estates " had been made out of it. Most of the huge estates of which we hear were in regions where there cannot have been a vast quantity of public land—as Etruria and Apulia.

'*Page* 13.—Probably Cicero was quite moderate, compared with the *optimates* generally, in his criticisms of the Gracchi. *Cf.* " Leg. Agr.," ii., § 10 : " Non sum is consul qui, ut plerique, nefas esse arbitrer Gracchos laudare, quorum consiliis, sapientia, legibus multas esse video rei publicæ partes constitutas." And *ibid.*, § 31 : " Si, Gracchi æquitate et pudore." I think your statement of Cicero's kindness to the faults of the aristocrats is hardly justified. His letters show extraordinary keenness of political vision, and in numerous places he criticizes most cuttingly the party with which, on the whole, he felt compelled to act. Surely Cæsar was one of the most corrupt and unscrupulous men of his time. Only his intellectual ascendency prevents this from being seen. And, of his officers, many who were good soldiers were in other respects among the worst men of their time. No instrument was too base for Cæsar's use.

'*Pages* 13, 14.—I believe the public sense of the Romans during the Republic was always against corruption and extortion. This is shown by the fact that laws to repress these were always popular and readily carried. There was neither hypocrisy nor mockery about this legislation. The ineffectualness of these laws was inevitable so long as the Republican constitution remained. We see this clearly, but a Roman patriot may be forgiven for not seeing it. I do not think that Cæsar's law was any more efficacious than the rest. It was with the ascendency of Augustus that the great change came. As to the opposition to Cæsar's laws, it must not be forgotten that he and his associates had established a veritable reign of terror in the capital. There is, I believe, no evidence that Cæsar ever contemplated anything like " popular " representation of the provinces. He admitted a few Gauls to the Senate, but that is another matter.

' *Page* 14.—It is remarkable how little remains to show what kind of new constitution Cæsar intended to " build up." He left to Augustus rather warnings to avoid than examples to follow.

' *Page* 15.—The letter opens up the whole question of the ancient views of " tyrannicide "—a large and difficult one.

' *Page* 16.—Have you not forgotten the *lex Tullia de*

ambitu, which for the first time made *exile* a strictly technical punishment? also the endeavour of Cicero to abolish the huge abuse of the *libera legatio?* And surely it is to be remembered that Cæsar was *in power,* and that Cicero never was, in any strict sense of the phrase.

'With regard to the law of Rullus, it ought to be remembered that this was not merely an agrarian law. It was designed to have far-reaching and, indeed, world-wide political consequences. There is much to show that Cicero was not opposed to agrarian laws pure and simple. He supported one in the year 60. He gave solid and sensible reasons for opposing that passed by Cæsar in 59. But, be it observed, the provisions of the law of Rullus which Cicero had condemned were not embodied in the law of 59, and, indeed, were never brought forward again. And can your remarks about the *proscriptorum liberi* be justified? Our information about the agitation in 63 is most defective. Clearly, however, in spite of the apparent justice of the cause, the agitation achieved little, which shows how strong the obstacle in the way must have been generally felt to be. Also, does not Cæsar's own action show this? So far as we know, from the time when he came into power on January 1, 59, till he had driven Pompeius out of Italy, he never lifted a finger to help the *proscriptorum liberi.* Is it likely, then, that Cicero, whose power at all times was small, could have done anything for the victims, even if he had made himself their champion? That he sympathized with them is well attested. It is curious that the only passage which connects Cæsar at all with the agitation of 63 is a very vague one in Vell. Pat., ii. 43, which is not above suspicion.

'*Page* 17.—How much ambition, how much patriotism, lay in Cæsar's course is hard to determine. I find the evidence of the former everywhere; to find evidence of the latter requires search and interpretation.

'*Page* 18.—I think that if the literature bearing on Cæsar's consulship be carefully examined, it will be seen that Pompeius was still, and, indeed, for long after, in the eyes of Rome, an indefinitely greater man than Cæsar.

' *Page* 22.—Is not all this about Cæsar's Divine ancestry merely traditional ?   It had probably appeared in funeral orations of the family for many generations, and would have been missed if Cæsar had omitted it.   There are parallels, of course, in not a few other families.

' *Page* 33.—The Helvetii were driven back by Cæsar, and a good many of them massacred ; but they were prominent at a later time under Vespasian, and even later still.   By the way, I think it quite possible that Cæsar's expression, *hostium loco habuit*, points to enslavement, not massacre.'

[Professor Reid's able defence of Cicero and the Senate reminds us how hard it is to do justice both to Cæsar and to Cicero and the ' *boni*.'

The question whether it was possible for Cæsar to maintain the Republican Constitution is a difficult one. Was it, or was it not, impossible for him to use his great power to reform the Senate, and restore it to efficiency as a governing body ?   Cæsar might have attempted this. He might also justly think that the hour for this had gone by.   Sulla's legislation had had disastrous effects on the morale of the ruling class.   The Senate was now so embittered by party feeling, so blinded by self-seeking, so determined to yield no jot of unjust privilege, that the first step towards a just Government was to break its power.   For the meantime, no other course was possible. The rights of the citizens of the Empire could now be safeguarded only by an absolute ruler.   Scotland is not the only country where King and commons have stood together against an unpatriotic and lawless nobility.

The Empire, it is true, resulted in moral degeneration for the ruling class.   But is it fair to estimate what Cæsar purposed from what the Empire actually became during its first three centuries after his untimely death ?   No ; it was not for this that Cæsar broke the tyranny of the aristocracy.

Cæsar did not admit his generals or his political fellow-
workers to share his plans.   Could a reformed Senate
have been trusted to do so ?   Cæsar must have felt that
any scheme for founding a great new Commonwealth,
in which Italians and provincials should have equal
rights, was too vast for any of his contemporaries to rise
up to.

Doubtless it is true that Cæsar often made use of corrupt men.   As Gaston Boissier has said : ' Honourable
men were found chiefly among the vanquished.'[1]   But
what hope was there for the State in men like Cato, or in
the worthier men of Cato's party, who, when the reality
of liberty was lost, laid such stress on the form of it ?
Such men, who live in an unreal world, may be more
dangerous to their country than the most corrupt poli-
tician.

The crisis was so extreme that Cæsar, it would seem,
could plan only for the immediate needs of the time both
in Italy and in the provinces.   It may be that he over-
looked the danger to Italy itself of establishing an heredi-
tary monarchy.   The problem which he undertook to
solve was, perhaps, too large for any one man.   But for
centuries the provinces reaped the full gain.   Cæsar was
cut off before he had time fully to develop his plans.
During the five and a half years from his reaching absolute power to his death he fought seven campaigns, and
spent only fifteen months in Rome.[2]   The time was too
short to plan for the future as well as the present.   Surely
Cæsar's admission of Gauls and libertines to the Senate
was most significant, even if it were merely the promise
of a true reorganization of that body, which at the time
would have been impossible.   As yet the head of the
State had to be independent of the Senate.   That body,
if made truly representative, might have expressed the
feeling of the country in naming the man most competent
for its head, even as in old days the King had been
elected by the Senate and their choice confirmed by the

---

[1] ' Cicéron et ses Amis.'   [2] Mommsen, v. 441.

people. If any man ever valued efficiency, Cæsar did. How strange that he should not have foreseen the dangers of a régime for the efficient working of which everything depended on one man, and demanded from him almost superhuman ability and energy ! By how strange an irony could Julius Cæsar be succeeded in the power he founded by a Nero ! Had he been spared for ten years longer, the State visibly more prosperous every year and party rancour weakening, a different policy would have been possible ; and with entirely new problems before him, no one living can tell how Cæsar's subtle genius might have solved them. Who can say if he might not even have waived his tribunitial power ?[1]

Because we admire Cæsar we need not depreciate Cicero. The Orator, with all his splendid gifts and great public spirit, was unfit to cope with the terrible times he lived in ; unfortunate as the leader of an unworthy and an ungrateful party ; unfortunate, too, as having supplied the chief evidence against himself in his own private letters. Many of these are, as Sellar calls them, ' the sincerest and most unreserved self-revelations which one man ever made to another,' yet they have been ungenerously interpreted as if they were ordinary historical documents.

I may refer, in conclusion, to Professor R. Y. Tyrrell's able and most interesting introductions to his edition of Cicero's letters. In vol. iii., p. xciv, he writes :

' Cæsar had a fixed determination to be the first man in the State. It was well for humanity that he became so. The century of Senatorial domination had been one of the worst ages for the world which it ever endured ; the period of the early Empire was one of the best which it ever enjoyed.' Yet he can write thus : ':To us Cæsar appears one of the most fortunate of men, and *the* most consummate and varied intellect that ever lived ; but he had no moral nature. All his seemingly generous actions

---

[1] This enabled him to initiate legislation, and to sit as assessor in the high courts.

would appear to have been directed by calculation of expediency. . . . In the means he adopted to obtain his ends, he did not rise one inch above the ordinary morality of his day.'

And yet this cold monster's pathetic *Et tu, Brute* has voiced the world's sense of treachery to friendship ever since !

Professor Tyrrell admits Cæsar's merit in ' effecting the destruction of the wicked oligarchy of Rome.'[1] Supposing Cæsar had left his task to others, who could have effected it ? Could Pompey ? or Cicero ? From the moment that Cæsar should have resigned his military supremacy his life was forfeited. In that crisis of the world, gifts so unique as his constituted a Divine right to rule. As to ' reforming the Senate,' would it have been any easier to create ideals of patriotism or morality in the Senate of Rome than to teach the Jewish Sanhedrin in the days of Caiaphas what religion meant ?—J.M.]

' *Page* 24.—Virgil, Eclogue IV. None of the three essays just published in a volume on " Virgil's Messianic Eclogue " [the writers are J. B. Mayor, W. W. Fowler, R. S. Conway], nor Professor W. M. Ramsay's articles in the *Expositor* for 1907, have convinced me that anything Jewish is reflected in Eclogue IV. Everything alleged is capable of better explanation.'

[Professor Mayor thinks that Virgil did not know Isaiah directly, but only through the medium of the Sibylline books. Through these the thoughts and expressions of the prophet ' filtered through to the poet.' Yet how could the poor shadow of Isaiah reflected in these verses have impressed the great Roman poet so profoundly ? The long succession of civil wars in Italy during some hundred years before Augustus had produced in Rome a strong sense of not merely moral degradation, but also of national guilt, which finds voice in the close of the first Georgic. As Professor Conway says : ' During the terrible century before Augustus (say from

---

[1] ' Correspondence of Cicero,' vol. iii., p. xciv.

133 to 31 B.C.) . . . Italy had seen twelve separate civil
wars, six of which had involved many of the provinces ;
a long series of political murders, beginning with the
Gracchi and ending with Cæsar and Cicero ; five deliberate,
legalized massacres,' and so on.[1] The soil of Italy was
foul with the blood of slaughtered citizens. Virgil tells
us how Nature protested against this unnatural course
of crimes by many a sign, and notably by the portentous
Julium Sidus, the great comet which flamed in the heavens
soon after the murder of Julius Cæsar. Men laid the guilt
of this long civil strife to the ambition of the rival leaders,
which they might well call ' mad ' and ' impious.' ' It
is the same feeling,' says Professor W. M. Ramsay, ' that
everyone who lives in Constantinople at the present day
becomes conscious of. It arises from the inevitable perception that one is in an atmosphere of decay, degeneration, degradation, and that there is no improvement to
be hoped for.' It is thus the more surprising that Virgil's
poem furnishes a remarkable exception to this universal
feeling of his time, since it prophesies for the world the
regeneration which it needed. ' Horace recognized,' he
continues, ' that the Republican party was incapable and
dead, and that Rome had nothing to hope from it, even
if it had been successful in the fight. Every reader of
his works knows that such was his feeling and such was
the widespread feeling of the Roman world. Men recognized . . . that the Republican party had failed decisively
to govern the Empire.' This utter disheartenment finds
voice in the Sixteenth Epode, when Horace calls upon all
true patriots to abandon Rome, and sail far away into
the ocean and seek a new world in those fabled ' Happy
Islands,' where the earth brings forth all her fruits in
abundance, and her powers are not tainted because of the
sins of men. This poem expresses, of course, no serious
suggestion or belief, except in so far as it gives voice to
the despair of Romans over the lost greatness of their
country. Horace is bidding men seek refuge in a dream,

---

[1] ' Virgil's Messianic Eclogue,' 1907, p. 34.

in which they might forget the actual facts of the Roman
State. Men felt that ' the old Rome could not stand ;
the Republican and aristocratic party, which had fought
to maintain the old Rome, was mistaken and practically
dead, and its policy had utterly failed. The poem is
really the expression of a despairing acquiescence in the
tyranny of the Triumvirate and the autocracy of the
coming Empire.'[1]

Ramsay considers that Virgil's Eclogue was written
towards the end of 40 B.C., a little later than Horace's
Sixteenth Epode, two phrases from which Virgil quotes
as a compliment to the younger and as yet little-known
poet. Virgil's answer to Horace is that the Golden Age
which he relegates to the land of dreams is already
beginning in Italy itself.

As to Virgil's acquaintance with Isaiah, or passages
from him, have scholars realized the significance of the
fact that in the Jewish synagogues to be found in every
Greek or Roman city strangers were made welcome ?
Many Greeks and Romans were devout worshippers in
these local synagogues, and from this class especially
St. Paul derived the nucleus of the churches founded by
him. We cannot doubt that in these Hellenistic synagogues the service was as a rule in Greek, the Hebrew
lessons being translated by the interpreter, who stood
beside the reader, the lessons from Moses being rendered
one verse at a time, we are told, and those from the
Prophets several verses together.[2] How else, indeed,
could the Gentiles join in the worship ? Thus, any
cultivated Roman of inquiring mind such as Virgil
might easily become acquainted with Isaiah's Messianic
prophecies.—J.M.]

'*Page* 19.—Book II., line 47: "Fervere cum videas
classem lateque vagari." I am tempted to write a little

[1] *The Expositor*, June and August, 1907.
[2] See the article 'Synagogue,' by Dr. Ginsburg, in Kitto's
'Cyclopædia of Biblical Literature,' third edition, 1876.

about this curious line. I have long thought that *classem* is used, not of the fleet, but of a military detachment, an archaism used by Virgil among others (" Æneid," vii. 716 and iii. 602 ; and in other scattered references, Anthol., I. 115, 3, *femineam classem*). This use found in an authority led Livy into a ridiculous blunder in IV. 34, 6. I am led to this by the great unlikelihood that Lucretius would mention a fleet in connection with high Roman officers. Sea command was usually deemed subordinate ; partly, also, by the word *vagari*, which is unsuitable to ships, but right for military evolutions. The technical word in prose is *evagari*, but as that will not go into verse Virgil uses the simple verb for it in " Æneid," v. 560 : " Tres equitum numero turmæ ternique vagantur ductores." It is quite a custom with Lucretius (as with some other authors, notably Tacitus) to substitute simple for compound verbs —so *firmare* often for *affirmare* or *confirmare*.

' *Page 25.*—It is remarkable that in many books the taurobolium should be connected with Mithras ; there is no authority for it. It belongs to the Magna Mater only. She was officially adopted in 205 B.C., but it is difficult to trace Mithras, even privately, in Italy much before the end of the first century A.D.'

[According to Percy Gardner, in his ' Exploratio Evangelica,' p. 333, when Pompey in 67 B.C. overcame the Cilician pirates, some of whom he settled in Italy, the worship of their deity, Mithras, spread slowly over the Roman Empire. Possibly a new worship of such a kind might not for a considerable time challenge public opinion by setting up inscriptions. Numerous monuments of Mithraic worship were found at Borcovicus, on the Roman wall in Northumberland (see the illustrations in the Handbook to the Museum at Chesters, 1903, pp. 175-196).—J.M.]

[*Page 37.*—As to the criticism on Lucretius's poem in Cicero's letter to his brother, I have to admit the justice of Professor R. Y. Tyrrell's strictures on my insertion of *non* before *multæ*. I have here followed Sellar ; Munro inclines to the same view. Tyrrell writes :

' No critic should be rash enough to change the logical quality of a proposition as it stands in the MSS. unless that proposition is demonstrably an impossible one, and unless he can show how it came to stand in that form in the MSS. . . . The criticism of his brother, with which Cicero expresses his agreement, is that Lucretius had not only much of the *genius* of Ennius and Attius, but also much of the *art* of the new school of poetry, which might seem incompatible with that genius. Now, whether genuine *afflatus* and minute perfection of execution are incompatible is a question which may be argued. To us it appears that they are not. Tennyson and Milton (not to bring in Shakespeare) have both. But even now some deny genius to Tennyson because of his perfect art. The criticism, whether true or false, is perfectly possible and intelligible.'—*Academy*, January 18, 1908.

Professor Reid had already written me to the same effect : ' I doubt whether *tamen* makes the insertion of *non* necessary. It is difficult to think that Cicero, if he read the poem at all, denied either the genius or the art. His own experiments in the *Aratea* surely would enable him, if nothing else could, to see the *ars*.'

This view, no doubt, is the correct one. But it seems to me that, if we are to keep the MS. reading, *ars* must be used here in the sense of ' Science,'[1] as referring specially to Lucretius's exposition of the atomic theory. *Ars* cannot here mean ' artistic treatment,' as in Ovid's line referring to Callimachus—

'Quamvis ingenio non valet, arte valet.'

Cicero could have seen nothing in common, but the very reverse, between Lucretius's method of treatment

---

[1] It is used of mathematics at Cic., ' De Orat.,' i. 3, 10. In the following passage it answers pretty exactly to our ' science ' : ' Si ars ita definitur . . . ex rebus penitus perspectis planeque cognitis atque ab opinionis arbitrio sejunctis scientiaque comprehensis ' (*ibid.*, i. 23, 108 ; *cf.* 92).

and that of Callimachus or Euphorion. Any intelligent
person who had for the first time read the poem could
not fail to be impressed by two points—namely, the
poetic genius shown, and the strange choice of Science
for the subject-matter; and this is what struck the
Ciceros.—J.M.]

'*Page* 51.—Doubtless the *Lex Cornelia* included *ama-
torium poculum* under the head of *veneficium*, but the
punishment of work in the mines (for *humiliores*) and of
relegatio (for *honestiores*) was only introduced in the time
of the Empire, perhaps under Tiberius.

'*Page* 59.—*Cf.* Cicero, "Leg.," where it is said that he
has two *patriæ*. A provincial doubtless used the word in
both ways.

'*Page* 61.—It is curious that the vetoing of the *Lex
Curiata*—an obvious means of obstruction—is never heard
of till the end of the Republic.

'*Page* 68.—V. 1190. I am glad to see that, spite of
Lachmann, Housman, and others, you think *severa* the
right reading. Apuleius often refers to Lucretius, and
seems in "De Deo Socr.," 121, to refer to this line : "*Pictis*
noctibus severa gratia, torvo decore." Also he refers,
ibid., to line 575 of this book, and in 117 to lines 705, 727.

'*Page* 73.—Horace, like Lucilius, used Stoic and Epicurean commonplaces pretty indiscriminately.

'*Page* 74.—The problem of the non-mention of Lucretius
has, of course, many parallels. Virgil had little occasion
to mention contemporary poets. He could hardly do so
in the "Æneid," and he went out of his way to bring in
the allusion to Lucretius in the "Georgics." Horace has
no mention of Propertius, and only one casual compli-
mentary reference to Catullus and Calvus.

'*Page* 91.—It may be physically true that the atoms
of Lucretius would not act as he supposes them to act if
they were not elastic. But can he have been conscious
of this ? Would he not have said that elasticity implied
void in the constitution of the atom, and was therefore
impossible ?

'*Page* 91.—*Minimæ partes*. It would take too long to discuss the *minima pars*, but I believe that it is merely a unit of comparison. The relation of size between the atoms required the supposition of such a unit.

'*Page* 98.—Lucretius really seemed to think that infinite subdivision would lead to the disappearance of matter altogether.

'*Page* 100.—As to the "mere guess," it must be remembered that the endless debates concerning the One and the Many must have led to the conception of the *atom* sooner or later.

'*Page* 111.—I. 1041. I see that you take *aversa viai* together, along with most editors, but I doubt the possibility of such a Grecism in Lucretius, or of *regione viai*, as in ii. 249. If the reading be right, it would be necessary to construe *ratione viai* together, " some principle governing its course," as in v. 81—*aliqua divom ratione*. *Cf.* also *aliqua ratione aversa* in v. 413, *aliqua ratione revictæ*, v. 409, so also i. 593. But there are obvious objections, and I think Lucretius wrote *regione . . . viarum*. *Cf.* i. 958, *nulla regione viarum;* Virgil's " Æneid," ix. 385. *fallitque timor regione viarum*.

'*Page* 113.—Of course, the comparison of the world with a ζῷον (also the stars) was very old, and naturally led to the idea, apart from atomism, of growth, decay, and death.

'*Page* 117.—II. 61—*naturæ species*. I have always felt a difficulty about *speciem videndi* in i. 321. If the reading is genuine, *species* there must mean " our power of vision," as in iv. 242, and *videndi* must be an explanatory or equivalent genitive, as in *Tartara leti*, etc. But Ovid, who sometimes has a reminiscence of Lucretius, has in " Trist.," ii. 531, " Invida me *spatio* natura coercuit arto," which looks like an echo of this. In Lucretius, ii. 61, *species* must be used passively—" what we see in nature," her " fair face."

'*Page* 126.—*Concilium* is usually, like *congressus*, a rendering of Epicurus's ἄθροισμα, but as not every ἄθροισμα results in a *res*, Lucretius usually restricts it to one that does.

'*Page* 128.—Cicero ("Fin.," i. 18-20 and elsewhere) argues that the concourse of atoms could not be creative. No doubt this contention goes back to the earliest criticisms of the atomic theory.

'*Page* 131.—The εἴδωλα. The difficulties of the εἴδωλα are endless, and one wonders that Lucretius sees so few of them—*e.g.*, when the εἴδωλον of a man comes from his body, do the separate atoms fly off and then reform in man's shape outside? If so, why should they ever reform? If the εἴδωλον comes off as a whole, how does it get free from the body without being rent to pieces? And, if rent, how is it put together again? And so on.

'*Page* 133.—

> ' Partibus e cunctis infernaque suppeditantur
> Ex infinito cita corpora materiai.'
>
> I. 1000, 1001 (Munro).

I believe *inferneque* is the right reading, as I used to contend thirty years ago in lectures. I never published this, but Postgate has since.[1] In your note, *cf.* κάτωθέν τε ὑπερείσουσι in the Œnoanda inscription (§ 20 Usener, 44 Heberdey and Kalinka), followed by καὶ συνάξουσι, which word may be the origin of *confulta* in Lucretius.

'*Page* 146 (*note*).—Is there any reason to think lightning an exception to the rule that no substance consists *entirely* of one sort of atoms? And, again, roundness is relative, like all else. The atoms of lightning need not be conceived as *absolutely* without irregularities.

'*Page* 158.—The question of the size of the sun is interesting. I have treated it partly in a note on "Acad.," ii. 82. There is no doubt that, for whatever reason, Epicurus thought that fire was an exception to the rule that apparent size diminishes with distance. This he treats as an ἐνάργημα—*i.e.*, a self-evident fact, needing no argument (Diog. L., x. 91). The Stoic objector in Philod., περὶ σημείων, urges that, in the view of Epicurus, the sun became one of the μοναχά, isolated

---

[1] *Journal of Philology*, xxiv. 133.

phenomena to which ἀναλογία does not apply. But it
was just by ἀναλογία that he supported his position.
From his ἐνάργημα he argues to the sun. As the diminu-
tion of objects by distance is attributed to the wearing-
down of the εἴδωλα as they pass through the air, we
must suppose that Epicurus imagined the εἴδωλα of fire
to be exempt from this wear and tear. (Diels, " Doxo-
graphi," p. 221, errs egregiously about this matter.) The
problem seems to have been handled in the treatise of
which the Herculaneum Manuscript, No. 1013, has preserved a few miserable fragments (Scott, p. 311) ; also,
of course, in Epicurus's περὶ φύσεως (Usener, §§ 80, 81).

' *Page* 160.—The reported gigantic remains accidentally
discovered in mining or opening up the earth, with natural
exaggerations as reports passed from mouth to mouth
(to which there are many scattered references in ancient
literature), may have been in Lucretius's mind when he
speaks of earth's youth.

' *Page* 160.—Of course, the passage about Epicurus,
having transcended the ramparts of the universe, must
have had many parallels in Greek literature. *Cf.* Timon
apud Sextus " adv. Math.," i. 305 (address to Pyrrho)—
μοῦνος δ᾽ ἀνθρώποισι Θεοῦ τρόπον ἡγεμονεύεις | ὅς περὶ πᾶσαν
ἐλὼν γαῖαν ἀναστρέφεται | δεικνὺς εὐτόρνου σφαίρας περι-
καύτορα κύκλον. It is even possible that Lucretius
imitated this.

' *Page* 161.—Lucretius, v. 802-804 are, I am sure, out
of place.

' *Page* 162.—Lucretius, v. 823—*prope certo*. The *prope*
is odd. Why should Lucretius qualify *certo* here ? The
adjective stands unqualified in parallel passages. Moreover, this is the only place in the text of Lucretius where
the noun *animal* occurs. I conjecture that he really
wrote *animantem in certo*, and that, when *animal* crept
in, the line was doctored.

' *Page* 171.—The infinite variation in individuals is, of
course, a main pillar of Darwinism and all forms of
Evolutionary doctrine.

' *Page* 206.—The language of Lucretius about " the soul of the soul " really does imply that it lives in a den by itself (*in cavea*), in spite of what he says elsewhere.

' *Page* 255.—*Simulacra meandi* is an odd expression. As there are no εἴδωλα of abstractions, it stands for images either of the person himself or of others in the act of walking, which are floating about in the air and meet him. Action is, therefore, always prompted by sheer accident, if this be pursued to its logical consequence. The answer given in iv. 777 *et seq.* is inadequate.

' *Page* 270 (*note*).—It may be a reminiscence of Lucretius which makes Ovid (" Her.," x. 95) represent the deserted Ariadne as fearing to look up at the sky—*timeo simulacra deorum.*

' *Page* 298.—Lucretius, v. 523-525—" Flammea per cælum pascentis corpora passim " (of the stars). Many years ago a theory of the maintenance of solar energy was put forward by Siemens, which reminded me of these lines. He supposed that the sun, moving through space, encounters myriads of meteorites, which burst in on the sun's envelope, and add to its heat.

' *Page* 305.—Plato, " Theæt.," p. 155. I have long been convinced that Campbell is wrong. The people who will not accept what they cannot grip (ἀπρὶξ ὄνυξι) are the followers of Antisthenes, who deny the existence of everything which is not concrete.

' *Page* 308.—St. Paul (2 Cor. v. 1). It is curious to remember that St. Paul's use of σάρξ goes back to Epicurus.

' *Page* 321.—The more I study Epicureanism and Stoicism, the more I am struck by the similarity rather than the difference between the two ethical systems.

' *Page* 341.—Style of Epicurus. I should hardly call Epicurus's prose halting. In addition to my note on Cicero's " Acad.," i. 5 (where *volgaris sermo* = ἡ πάνδημος φράσις in Philodem. (" Rhetorica " ed. Sudhaus, p. 164), *cf.* what Usener says in " Epicurea," Preface, pp. xli, xlii. The abuse of his style in the ancient writers merely implies that he set at naught the conventional rules current in the rhetorical schools. *Cf.* Athen., v., p. 187, where, speaking of the συμπόσιον of Epicurus, he sneers at τὴν ἐπιτρέχουσον τῇ λέξει ἀρρυθμίαν.'

[Usener refers to Epistle III. for its well-balanced periods, elegant language, and especially the avoidance of hiatus, as contrasting with Epicurus's usual careless-ness of style—' Ipsam styli elegantiam ab Epicuro non solum neglectam sed etiam contemptam.' This might arouse doubts as to its authenticity, ' but who can affirm that Epicurus, if he chose to do so, could not also have written with care and elegance ?' And Usener reminds us that Epicurus had been a pupil of Nausiphanes, who gave great attention to rhetoric. Most of Epicurus's works belong to the class of ὑπομνήματα, or ' *commentarii*,' written not for the cultivated public, but for himself and his followers ; hence, Usener says, the lack of atten-tion to form which he is justly charged with by ancient writers (p. xlii).—J.M.]

' *Page* 342.—παιδεία in Epicurus is not quite our " culture."

' *Page* 412 (*note*).—I myself remember Clifford as an extreme High Churchman.'

ADDENDA

1. *Vol. I., p.* 46.—The unfinished condition of the poem. In the close of his ' Note Lucreziane ' (Turin, 1900), which forms an appendix to his edition, Giussani discusses the subject of lacunæ and transpositions in the text of the poem with special reference to Heinze, who is in this respect very conservative.

2. *Vol. I., p.* 48.—A high authority on mental ailments, Dr. W. W. Ireland, agrees with me in rejecting (see p. 50) Stampini's theory that Lucretius suffered from epilepsy. He says :

' There is no evidence that Lucretius ever suffered from epilepsy, and the statement that Napoleon was an epileptic, even if it were correct, bears little upon the question. Tasso was, no doubt, insane, but his writings, after he became deranged, showed a marked falling off. The case of Auguste Comte would be a better illustration. Philtres were much in vogue in those times, furnished by a disreputable class, who seem to have used large doses of powerful drugs, such as henbane or stramonium, which disordered the intellect. Although the use of a philtre to make a person fall in love with a given individual is a superstition, it might reduce the subject to a condition in which the will-power was deficient, and the sensual desires were excited.'—*Journal of Mental Science,* January, 1908.

3. *Vol. I., p.* 129.—Giussani's assumption that Lucretius and Epicurus assert the existence of ' molecules ' as well as of ' atoms.' In his ' Note Lucreziane,' p. 22, Giussani is disposed to defend this opinion—so far, at least, as Epicurus is concerned. Epicurus, he claims, uses ὄγκοι first in the sense of *partes minimæ* of the atom, and, secondly, in that of ' molecules ' of compound substances, such as water, wine, marble. Giussani thinks that Lucretius may have misunderstood the term when he found it in Epicurus's texts in this second meaning.

4. *Vol. I., Chapter X.*—Atomic Declination and Free-will. In
a note at the close of the ninth edition of Zeller's ' Grundriss
der Geschichte der griechischen Philosophie ' (1909), Dr.
Lortzing says : ' Whether Epicurus actually wished to base
human Free-will upon the Declination of the atoms is a matter
not precisely established, since the evidence for this in
Lucretius, Cicero, and Plutarch is confirmed by no direct
statement of Epicurus himself in our documents.'
No Epicurean doctrine is more clearly attested than
Atomic Declination as explaining our Free-will. The passages
in Lucretius and in Cicero (' De Fato,' x. 22, 46 ; ' De
Nat. Deorum,' i. 69) are amply sufficient to prove this.
Plutarch's slight references are of the vaguest. All recent
research confirms the close adherence of Lucretius to his
master's teaching in every detail.
When this doctrine is not only so well attested, but forms
one of Epicurus's cardinal tenets, how are we to explain the
absolute silence of Diogenes Laertius, and of the Epicurean
epistles included by him on this subject ? This is, indeed, a
puzzle. Not that it in any way justifies us in doubting our
evidence that Epicurus based Free-will on this doctrine. I
am inclined to fancy that Diogenes (who is thought himself to
have been an Epicurean), seeing the notion that atoms have
the power to swerve from their path jeered at on all sides,
may have resolved to avoid reference to this doctrine, and to
omit documents bearing on it in order to save his master's
credit. But in any case the silence of Diogenes as to this
leading doctrine is a notable warning not to press too strongly
the argument *ex silentio.*
5. *Vol. I., p. 247.*—Theory of Images. As bearing upon
Lucretius's attempt to explain their efflux, I may call attention to J. P. Postgate's able emendation of iv. 193. ' Primum
quod parvula causa *Sat* procul a *tergost* quæ provehat atque
propellat ' he renders thus : ' The idola which bodies give off
can pass over vast spaces in a marvellously short time, since
(*ubi*) they are so light that the smallest impulse—*i.e.*, whatever it is that causes them to be detached from the bodies
that give them off—is enough to send them flying great
distances through space.' Curiously, Giussani misses the
point of the emendation by taking *sat* with *procul* (' Note
Lucreziane,' p. 42).
6. Texts of the poem by Pontanus and Marullus. I
have called attention to hitherto unknown copies of each of
these texts, the former in the British Museum, the latter in
the Bibliothèque Nationale at Paris.[1] The former is completely ready for the printer, with preface by Girolamo

[1] *Journal of Philology*, No. 46, 1895 ; *Classical Review*, July, 1897.

Borgia (see p. 3 of this volume). Both copies are made on the margins of the Venice edition of 1495.

On the title-page of the volume containing Marullus's text are the words, 'Petri Martellij liber est.' According to Jovius ('Elogia doctorum vivorum,' Antwerp, 1557), Martellus was a friend of Crinitus, one of Marullus's most intimate friends, who wrote some touching verses on the poet's tragic and premature death. The volume probably belonged to this P. Martellus. Some later owner of the book has appended a note which might possibly mean that these readings are due to Portanus. Instead of this the volume contains a very complete copy of the readings of Marullus.

Three hands are apparent in these notes. The first, to whom the great bulk of the notes are due, is that of a scholar with letters finely formed. The second hand has largely supplemented this in Books I. and II. Evidently both writers had before them Marullus's readings in manuscript. But the chief interest attaches to the third hand ; the strong and decided characters seem to indicate a man of action as well as a scholar. At vi. 357 this writer adds a Homeric illustration suggested by ' Pe. Monachus,' and immediately below he corrects *ventique calores* thus :

' Puto legendum. Ventique calore.'

This we know from Victorius to be an emendation by Marullus. The writer of this note in the first person was unquestionably Marullus himself. Throughout this volume he has most carefully revised the readings of the first hand, frequently correcting them, as well as adding fresh ones, including many variations which are not recorded by Munro. The Petrus Monarchus referred to, if not the same person, is probably a relative of the Severus Monachus from whom Pius (editor of the Bologna edition of 1511) borrowed a copy of Marullus's readings—' exemplar mira industria castigatum,' he calls it. This may be the one now in Paris.

Both these volumes, it would appear, give the latest thoughts of either scholar on the text. Pontanus's emendations were transcribed for Borgius in 1502, while Pontanus himself died in 1503. The Paris copy contains numerous readings by Marullus which do not, I believe, appear among his corrections of the Munich manuscript.

*   *   *   *   *

Vol. I., p. 28.—Note 1 : for ' family,' read ' family life ' ; note 2 : for ' Corinth,' read ' Ephesus.'

Vol. I., p. 33. — ' Other nations all but exterminated, like the Samnites and Etruscans.' Much as the Samnites suffered in the Social War, and also from Sulla (who declared

13—2

that the Samnites must be extirpated, since Rome would have no rest so long as Samnium existed), and the Etruscans also from Sulla, and his military colonies, this statement requires to be modified.

Vol. I., p. 80.—For ' two letters by Epicurus,' read ' three.' See Appendix II.

Vol. I., p. 411.—The translation from Goethe's ' Gesetz der Trübe ' misinterprets the verse, which refers to the poet's theory of colours.

Vol. II., Preface, pp. ix-x.—As bearing upon the question of literary versus abstract treatment of a subject, I may quote from Professor W. James's article on Henri Bergson in the latest *Hibbert Journal* (April, 1909).

Bergson holds that the function of the intellect is practical rather than theoretical. Those sciences which deal with space and matter, with the transformations of external things, are those in which it triumphs. ' When it deals with moral facts, with the inner movements of our spirits, then it has reached the end of its tether. . . . We know the inner movements of our spirits only perceptually [*i.e.*, through our deep feelings and intuitions]. We can give no distinct account of their elements.'

In explaining any experience by a series of concepts we have to deal with things that are discontinuous. ' The stages into which you analyze a change are *states:* the change itself goes on between them. It lies along the intervals. . . . To know adequately what really *happens* we ought to see into the intervals, but the mathematician sees only the extremity of these. He fixes a few results, he dots a curve, he substitutes a tracing for the reality.'' [Thus to note and mark off eight furlongs of a road is not the same thing as to walk a mile. A set of photographs showing the position of the players at regular intervals during a football match conveys no sense of what the game means to the players.]

The intellect gives us ' knowledge *about* things as distinguished from . . . sympathetic *acquaintance* with things : it touches only the outer surface of reality. The surface which such knowledge covers may indeed be enormous in extent . . . but it does not penetrate a millimetre into the solid dimension. . . . Thought deals thus solely with surfaces. It can name the thickness of reality, but it cannot fathom it, and its inefficiency is essential and permanent, not temporary. The only way in which to apprehend the reality's thickness is either to experience it directly by being a part of reality oneself, or to evoke it in imagination by sympathetically divining someone else's inner life.'

If, then, we truly wish to know the inner nature of reality,

we must turn our backs upon our concepts, and bury ourselves
in the ' thickness ' of the passing moments of the flux of life.
' Instead of intellectual knowledge being the profounder,
Bergson calls it the more superficial. The one thing it cannot
do is to reveal the inner nature of things. 'Dive back into the
flux, then,' Bergson tells us, ' if you wish to know reality.'

Professor James and Bergson have gone far to analyze and
justify the feeling of ordinary people that ' knowledge ' which
is not in constant touch with experience is an illusion—and an
illusion how misleading ! For broad and healthy minds
literature and philosophy supplement each other, and cannot
be dissociated. Such men are not in danger of being ridden
away with by their own logic. They know the limits of
philosophy, and see that ' there are some things which cannot
be discovered or detected, much less understood by the mere
reason.'[1] It is art, not philosophy, which brings us vitally
into contact with the Ideas and with reality. It alone is
capable of interpreting human life for us.

Professor James's contention carries weight not in philosophy merely, but very specially in the field of scholarship.
Often the scholar is not in a real or profound sense a student
of literature. The severe demands of scholarship in dis-
criminating usages, synonymes, and constructions[2] make him
less careful about grasping the full content of his author's
thought, and tend to vitiate his interpretation. This defect
is most notable in dealing with difficulties in the text, where
it is absolutely necessary to enter by imagination into the
poet's mind, and grasp not merely the ' motive ' of an entire
poem, but to realize by imagination the emotion and atmosphere
of the passage in question before a convincing emendation can
be made, not half a dozen suggestions each of different meaning,[3] which we may choose from, but the single one which
Ritschl's noble precept, ' There is not more than one right,'
demands. Imagination must here supplement reason and
scholarship, and light the way before them. In the field of
Latin poetry we can boast of three scholars notably gifted with
this power of grasping a writer's spirit and personality which
alone is the key to true exposition—Conington, Munro, and
Sellar. In these the Scholar and the Humanist are not
separated.

[1] 'Schopenhauer's Philosophy,' by W. Caldwell, 1896, p. 299. See
especially the two chapters on Schopenhauer's Philosophy of Art.
[2] To realize how severe these may be, we need only think of Sophocles
or Virgil.
[3] As is the practice of Blaydes, for example, who often offers us many
widely-varying and highly-ingenious conjectures on the same place of the
text of Sophocles. But almost as well might we offer a sculptor the choice
of several differently-fashioned limbs or features from which to restore
some noble statue of a Greek master.

INDEX

In both volumes the index is meant to be supplemented by the very full tables of contents—e.g., for 'Atoms (of Lucretius),' see both indices, and also Vol. I., pp. xiv and xv, containing contents of Chapters V. and VI.

	PAGES
ἄθροισμα	188
Analogy, Epicurus's use of .. Vol. I., 244, 296 ; Vol. II.,	190
Anima animæ	190
Anthropology, Lucretius's	120
Apuleius, influence of Lucretius on	187
Antisthenes	191
Aristippus	153–161
,, influenced by Socrates	155, 157
Aristotle, Gassendi attacks	20
,, on Spontaneity	89
Ars	186
Ataraxia the condition of Pleasure	167
Atomic Theory, criticism of scholastics on	49
,, ,, origin of	99, 188
,, ,, still indispensable as a working hypothesis	vi
Atom, the Daltonian	163
,, now supposed to be a composite structure ..	116
,, disintegration of	114–5
Atoms of Lucretius, combining properties of ..	vi, 95
,, ,, elasticity of	187
,, ,, parts of	188
,, ,, shapes of	111
αὐτοματισμὸς	82 (note)
αὐτόματον	89, 100
Balance of Forces	137
Benn, A. W., on Socrates	171
Bergson, Henri	196
Bockemüller, Friedrich	136
Borgia, Girolamo	3
Brett, Professor G. S.	43, 92

PAGES

Brieger, Dr. Adolf xiii
,, ,, on the original movement of the atoms .. 101
,, ,, on the letters of Epicurus .. 103–4
,, ,, discusses the doctrine of the Veracity of
the Senses 132–3
Bruno, Giordano 51
,, ,, God not only immanent, but transcendent 55
,, ,, the Inward Artificer 53
,, ,, Matter and Form are One 53
,, ,, Soul of the World 54

Cæsar and the Republic 179
,, his aims not realized 180
,, his *leges Juliæ* 177
Carneades 71
Cazræus, Peter 29
Certus 66, 77
'Chance' in Epicureanism 69–70, 82–84
Cicero, criticism attributed to.. 12
,, on the Gracchi 176
,, his letters, W. Sellar on 181
,, his verdict on Lucretius, J. S. Reid on 186
,, ,, ,, ,, Professor R. Y. Tyrrell on 186
Civilization, progress of 120
Clifford, W. K. .. .. viii, 192
Concilium 188
Confulta 189
Contract, the Social 126
Conway, Professor R. S., on the Civil Wars 182
Copernicus 33
Cyrenæicism 151–160
,, the New 161

Declination, 'threefold' (Guyau) 67
,, ,, (Giussani) 83
,, Professor G. S. Brett on 93
,, Silence of Diogenes Laertius as to the doctrine 194
Diderot 38, 60
Diels, Hermann 112, 190
Diogenes of Œnoanda 123, 124, 189
Duncan, Professor R. K. 114

'Eduction' of Forms 48
εἴδωλα .. Vol. I., 243, *seq.* ; Vol. II., 133, 148, 190, 191
,, difficulties of the theory 189
,, Lucretius's attempt to explain their emission .. 194

PAGES

Eleatic School and Atomism 99–100
Electrons, theory of 113
,, Sir Oliver Lodge on 115
,, Professor J. J. Thomson on 117
,, unproved hypotheses regarding .. 117–8
,, 'molecules of electricity' assumed 119
,, wherein the electron does not correspond to the
Lucretian atom vi
,, its bearing on the ultimate constitution of matter
summed up by Mr. Frederick Soddy 117–8
ἐνάργημα 189
Epicureans, list of Roman 6
,, ,, Reid, J. S., on 8–10
,, ,, its origin 9
,, ,, omissions in 10
Epicurus : his doctrine of Chance 69
,, his grasp of Law in Nature 69–70, 169–170
,, lays stress on ethics x
,, his letters 102
,, style of 192
,, had he an esoteric theology ? 147
ἐπιεικής 156
Euripides 104

'Faculties' of the Schoolmen 16
Fatum 75, 169
Fetichism 73
Fludde, Robert 34
Fœdera fati 75, 169
,, naturæ 75, 169
Forces, Balance of 137
Form, the First 55
Forms, Accidental 16, 30
,, 'Eduction' of 48
,, Substantial 31, 45, 52, 61
Free-will, Lucretius's argument for 128

Galileo 17
Gardner, Professor Percy 11
,, ,, ,, on Mithras worship 185
Gassendi attacks Aristotle 20
,, his interest in anatomy 41
,, first to observe transit of Mercury 24
,, his great work on Epicureanism 27
,, his ethics 37–39

PAGES

Gassendi, charged with atheism 29
,, place of atoms in his system 42
,, Professor Brett on 43, 92
,, what science owes him 41
Gautier, Joseph 19, 23
Giussani, Carlo .. xiii, 80, 83, 103-4, 131-3, 139, 140
,, ,, his ' Note Lucreziane ' 193
,, ,, on misplaced sections of the poem .. 193
Grote on Socrates and laws of Nature 171
Guyau, Jean-Marie .. .. xii, 62
,, ,, his doctrine of Spontaneity in things .. 63
,, ,, his new ethics 63
,, ,, misinterprets Lucretius .. 67, 77, 78
,, ,, on the Cyrenaics 159
,, ,, on Free-will and Hedonism 151
,, ,, on the evolution of Society 127
Gwatkin on Roman Religion 176

Harper, Thomas, S.J. 46
Hedonism. See Pleasure, doctrine of.
Helium 118
Hirzel 141, 145, 147-8
Hortensius, Q. 4, 5, 8
Hugo, Victor 124

ἰδέαι (denoting ' atoms ') 112
Ideas of Aristotle 50
,, of Plato 50
Ireland, Dr. W. W. 115, 124
,, ,, was Lucretius an epileptic? 193
Isaiah and Virgil 182
Isonomia 137
,, Giussani on 139
,, Professor Walter Scott on 139
Italy, devastation of.. 175

James, Professor W 108, 196
Jerome 5
,, refers to commentary on Lucretius 7

Lachelier 140, 143
Language, origin of 122, 126
Law in Nature, Epicurus's assertion of 69-70, 169-170
,, ,, did Socrates deny that such laws can be
discovered ? 171

PAGES

Leibnitz 17
,, his Monads 56
,, Zeller on the Monads 58
Leucippus : his atomic theory 99
Lightning (its atoms) 189
Lodge, Sir Oliver, on the Electron 115
,, ,, on Law and Guidance 108
,, ,, Conservation of Energy consistent with
Guidance 109
,, ,, Life not a form of Energy Vol. I., p. 189
Lortzing, Dr. Victor, on Declination and Free-will .. 194
Lucilius 6
Lucretius : his poetic quality .. Vol. I., xxiii–xxv, 68, 159, 259,
374, 383–398, 419–422, etc. ; Vol. II., 124
,, passages of the poem commented on by Pro-
fessor J. S. Reid .. .. ..
,, Book I., 321, p. 188 ; 958, p. 188 ; 1,000, p. 189 ; 1,041,
p. 188
,, Book II., 47, p. 184 ; 61, p. 188 ; 249, p. 188
,, Book IV., 242, p. 188 ; 777, p. 191 ; 881, p. 191
,, Book V., 81, p. 188 ; 413, p. 188 ; 802–4, p. 190 ;
823, p. 190 ; 1,190, p. 187

Martha, Constant 135
Marullus : copy of his text 194
Matter, scholastic view of 44
,, ultimate constitution of 117–119
Mayor, Joseph B. 141
,, ,, on esoteric Epicurean theology .. 147
Mithras worship, J. S. Reid on 185
Molecules, did Lucretius believe in ? 193
Mommsen on devastation of Italy 175
Mœnia mundi 190
Monads 56
μοναχὰ 189

Necessity 75, 77, 84

ὄγκοι 193
Ovid : reminiscences of Lucretius 188, 191

παιδεία (in Epicurus) 192
Parmenides 99
Partes minimœ 188, 193
Pater, Walter : ' The New Cyrenæicism ' 161
Patria (use of) 187

PAGES

Paul, St., and Epicurus 191
Peiresc, Nicolas 19, 35
Philodemus 146, 189, 191
Philtres : Dr. W. W. Ireland on 193
Piracy in Mediterranean 172
Plagæ 86
Plato (who is the materialistic philosopher referred to in
   ' Theætetus ' ?) 191
Pleasure, doctrine of 151–166
  ,,   ' the Good,' identified with Pleasure by Aristippus 153
  ,,   the pleasure of the moment 154
  ,,   modified by introducing the notion of the future.. 159
  ,,   divergence of Epicurus from Aristippus .. 160
  ,,   English Utilitarians.. 163–166
Plutarch on Declination 81
Pollius Parthenopæus 6, 11
Pontanus 3, 7
  ,,   copy of his text 194
  ,,   his repute as a scholar 13
Postgate, J. P. 190, 194
Pre-movement, Divine 105
Probus, Valerius 7
  ,,   ,,   his ' Life of Virgil ' 6
Proscriptorum liberi 178
Pulsford, John 106

Qualities, Occult 17

Radio-activity .. .. Vol. I., 105 ; Vol. II., 113
Radium, discovery of 113
Ramsay, Sir W. 118
Ramsay, Professor W. M., on the Roman sense of guilt
               for Civil Wars 183
  ,,   ,,   on Horace's Sixteenth Epode .. 183
  ,,   ,,   on Virgil's Fourth Eclogue .. 184
Reid, Professor J. S. : defence of Cicero 177–8
Rullus : his Agrarian Law 178

Sainte-Beuve ix
Sallust : debate in Senate 176
Schœmann, G. F. 141, 143–147
Schopenhauer .. .. x, 90
Scott, Professor Walter 139, 141–146
Sellar, W. Y. 168, 181
Semina rerum .. .. vi, 95
Senses, veracity of 132

PAGES

Sidgwick, Professor Henry 62, 88
Socrates on Law in Nature   171
Soddy, Frederick   117
Stampini, Ettore, on Cicero's criticism   13
στερέμνια 142, 144
Suetonius, life of Virgil   ..   Vol. I., 35 ; Vol. II., 5 (note)
Sun, size of   189
Swift, Jonathan   ix
Symonds, J. A.   136

Taurobolium   185
Tennyson 56, 59
Thomson, J. J.   117
Twofold Truth, doctrine of   32
Tyndall, Professor   viii
Tyrrell, Professor R. Y., on Cæsar   181
   ,,   ,,   on Cicero's estimate of Lucretius   186

ὑπομνήματα 192
Usener, Hermann 102, 103
   ,,   ,,   on style of Epicurus 192
Utilitarians, English   163–166

Varro, M. Terentius 12
Venus, Invocation to   135
Victorius, Petrus   195
Virgil called ' an Epicurean ' 6
   ,,   and Isaiah   182–184
Vis naturalis 75, 84

Ward, W. G.   105
Windelband   99
Woltjer, Dr. 7, 8, 12–13
World conceived as an organism   190

Zeller, Edward   xi
   ,,   ,,   on the Epicurean Gods 137, 143, 148
   ,,   ,,   on Guyau's theory of Spontaneity   .. 88
   ,,   ,,   on the original motion of the atoms   .. 101

THE END

BILLING AND SONS, LTD., PRINTERS, GUILDFORD